The Huge Quiz Book

by

Don Wilson

CLARION

Contents

Introduction

This book is for all those who enjoy quizzes, both those who set the questions and those who attempt to give the answers!

If you run quizzes, you can either pick and choose the questions you want to ask from this selection of 40 quizzes (each containing 100 questions), or you can simply ask a complete quiz directly from the book. To make it easy for quiz-setters, the answers are instantly to hand as each answer appears at the end of its question. This saves the quiz-setter from having to turn the page or search at the back of the book for the right answer – a procedure which sometimes results in the wrong answer being given!

If you enjoy participating in quizzes, you'll have great fun browsing through the book and testing your knowledge at leisure.

Whatever your interest in quizzes, I hope this book will give you many hours of enjoyment.

Don Wilson

Quiz 1

1. Who wrote *The Abbess of Crewe* and *A Far Cry From Kensington*? **Muriel Spark**

2. How many Parliamentary constituencies did Birmingham have in the 1992 General Election? **11**

3. From which country did Panama declare its independence in 1903? **Colombia**

4. Who partnered Martina Hingis to win the Women's Doubles at Wimbledon in 1996? **Helena Sukova**

5. Who was argued to be the author of the 'lost' novels *Sad Times* and *Miss Miles*? **Charlotte Brontë**

6. Who played Jeff Slade in the TV series *Crime Traveller*? **Michael French**

7. Which film actor was called 'The Muscles From Brussels'? **Jean-Claude Van Damme**

8. Are pepos ancient Spanish coins, volcanic vents or gourd fruits? **Gourd fruits**

9. True or false: by air Cairo is approximately 2,750 miles from London? **False (2,194)**

10. Who played the stewardess who had to fly the plane in the film *Airport 1975*? **Karen Black**

11. Which element has the chemical symbol Sc? **Scandium**

12. What would you listen to with a sphygmophone?
The pulse

13. What is the currency of both North and South Korea?
The Won

14. For what is the Jerwood Prize awarded?   **Modern Art**

15. Where are the islands of Brechou, Lihou and Jethou?
Channel Islands

16. What was a Sallee-man?   **A (Moorish) pirate**

17. Which art teacher and cartoonist created eccentric music festivals?   **Gerard Hoffnung**

18. Which word means to pull faces, a cleaning implement and a mass of hair?   **Mop**

19. Is the deepest sea the Caribbean, the South China or the Sea of Japan?   **Caribbean**

20. Which famous writer worked as 'Corneto di Bassetto', music critic for the *Star* newspaper?   **G B Shaw**

21. Who created the comic characters Pip, Squeak and Wilfred?   **Uncle Dick (Bertram Lamb)**

22. Off which continent is the Bight of Bonny?   **Africa**

23. Who hosted the TV talk show *The Show*?   **Bob Mills**

24. In ancient times, what were made from potin?   **Coins**

25. Which grain is sometimes called mealie?
Maize, Indian corn

26. Who played the deceitful lover in the 1949 film *The Heiress*?   **Montgomery Clift**

27. How is character judged in chirognomy?
From the lines in the hand

28. In which sport have March Conservatives, British Cellophane, Cowes Medina and Carlisle Courtfield all been winners? **Bowls**

29. Which state did George Washington represent in the 1st and 2nd Continental Congresses? **Virginia**

30. Who wrote *Too Damn Famous* and *Second Act*?
    Joan Collins

31. Is a rebarbative person surly, talkative or enthusiastic?
    Surly

32. To what was Captain Cook referring in 1771 when he wrote: ''Most perilous and extraordinary – astonishing and scarcely to be credited.''? **Surf-boarding!**

33. On which instrument would a planxty be played?
    A harp

34. Who played the title role in the 1948 film *Bonnie Prince Charlie*? **David Niven**

35. Who presented the TV series *Even Further Abroad*?
    Jonathan Meades

36. What did the Queen decide to do from April 6th, 1993?
    Pay income tax

37. Who was the last leader of the Liberal Party?
    David Steel

38. What did *Time* magazine refer to in 1934 as ''a phenomenon as well as a state''? **California**

39. True or false: the Royal Marines were formed in 1757?
    False (in the 1600s)

40. Who would wear a chimer or chimere? **A bishop**

41. Where did a dey-woman work? **In a dairy**

42. Under what name did Count Balthazar Klossowski de Rola find fame as an artist? **Balthus**

43. With which sport would you associate Kim Shaw, Lynette Horsburgh and Kelly Fisher? **Snooker**

44. For what did George Stephenson receive a public testimonial of £100? **His safety lamp**

45. Which famous brothers were members of the Oxford 'Holy Club'? **John and Charles Wesley**

46. In which film was Fluffy Bunny Feet needed on *Operation Sleepy Weasel*? ***Hot Shots!***

47. For what purpose was dunnage used in ships? **To keep cargo dry or secure**

48. With what is Kime's Directory concerned? **International Law**

49. In which country was Maria Callas born? **USA**

50. Who was the first person to ski alone and unaided to both Poles? **Borge Ousland**

51. Who wrote *Rose Madder* and *The Green Mile*? **Stephen King**

52. Is mousseline a creamy dessert, a fine muslin or mouselike? **Fine muslin**

53. What powers an ornithopter? **The aviator**

54. Which TV time travel series featured scientists Doug Phillips and Tony Newman? ***The Time Tunnel***

55. What is a croydon? **A two-wheeled gig**

56. Which city is served by Fiumicino airport? **Rome**

57. Who wrote *George, Don't Do That*? **Joyce Grenfell**

58. For which Rugby Union Club did Jonathan Davies sign in 1995? **Cardiff**

59. Which National Park's Information Office is at Dulverton? **Exmoor**

60. For what does the abbreviation DCL stand? **Doctor of Civil Law**

61. What is a coalmouse? **A bird**

62. Which country is separated from South America by the Serpent's Mouth and the Dragon's Mouth? **Trinidad and Tobago**

63. Which actress Dame had to learn Sioux for her role in the film *A Man Called Horse*? **Dame Judith Anderson**

64. Of which order is the Duke of Gloucester the Grand Prior? **The Order of St John**

65. What would you be playing if you achieved a capot? **Piquet (Cards)**

66. Who succeeded Edmund Ironside as King of England? **Cnut (Canute)**

67. Who wrote the bestselling book *Centennial*? **James Michener**

68. Which Canadian province was originally called the Red River Settlement? **Manitoba**

69. Who painted *Paradiso*, *Entombment* and *The Golden Calf*? **Tintoretto**

70. As a manufacturer of what did Eli Whitney make a fortune? **Firearms**

71. Are grey wethers wild sheep, blocks of sandstone or female grouse? **Blocks of sandstone**

72. In which capital city is the Omayed Mosque, the Tomb of Saladin and 'the street which is called Straight'?

Damascus

73. Which river forms the Delta Dunarii? **River Danube**

74. Who played the 'Minor' in the film *The Major and the Minor*? **Ginger Rogers**

75. After Greenland, which is the world's largest island?

New Guinea

76. Which word means the offspring of a male ass and a mare, an instrument for spinning cotton and a backless slipper? **Mule**

77. Is bumbo a children's game, a drink or the back of beyond? **A drink**

78. On TV who partnered Piggy Malone in his investigations? **Charlie Farley**

79. Which pirate had a ship called *Queen Anne's Revenge*?

Blackbeard

80. Which sports stadium in Yorkshire won the 1995 RIBA Building of the Year award? **Kirklees Stadium**

81. In which sport were Goole Avengers, Barnsley and District and Birkenhead Centre all divisional winners in 1995? **Angling**

82. Who wrote *Sophie's World*? **Jostein Gaarder**

83. Which strait separates the heel of Italy from Albania?
The Strait of Otranto

84. Is witches' butter a solution produced by insects, goose grease or an algae? **An algae**

85. What is Abell 3627? **A galaxy cluster**

86. What has 43,252,003,274,489,856,000 different patterns?
Rubik's Cube

87. Which word means a social class, a sequence and a mandate? **Order**

88. Where in New Jersey did the *Hindenburg* airship catch fire? **Lakehurst**

89. Who wrote, directed and starred in the film *The Plank*?
Eric Sykes

90. Which drink was advertised in the USA as "hits the spot,/ Twelve full ounces, that's a lot"? **Pepsi Cola**

91. Who would use a bistoury in his/her work?
A surgeon (It is a scalpel)

92. Who wrote: "Certain women should be struck regularly, like gongs."? **Noel Coward**

93. Which poet wrote *Old Pictures in Florence*, *Porphyria's Lover* and *Fra Lippo Lippi*? **Robert Browning**

94. True or false: Pam Dawber played Mindy in the TV series *Mork and Mindy*? **True**

95. Who wrote the operas *Angélique*, *Gonzague* and *Le Roi d'Yvetot*? **Jacques Ibert**

96. Who wrote *Confessions of an English Opium Eater*?
Thomas De Quincy

97. Whom did John Wayne lead into the Sahara in the film *Legend of the Lost*?
Rossano Brazzi (and Sophia Loren tagged along)

98. What form of shopping did Aaron Montgomery Ward begin in 1872? **Mail-order selling**

99. Who said: "He didn't riot. He got on his bike and looked for work."? **Norman Tebbitt**

100. On TV Blanche and Harry Morton lived next door to which comedy couple? **Burns and Allen**

Quiz 2

1. Which word means decayed wood, worthless articles and a youth movement? **Punk**

2. In which Geological Era did the Devonian Period occur? **Paleozoic**

3. Who had Top Twenty hits with *Private Life*, *Slave To The Rhythm* and *Pull Up To The Bumper*? **Grace Jones**

4. What is the address in London of Conservative Central Office? **32 Smith Square**

5. On TV who played Jane Eyre when Ciaran Hinds played Mr Rochester? **Samantha Morton**

6. Is prase a tropical seaweed, a type of quartz or long-winded chatter? **Quartz**

7. Which sport featured in the films *Body and Soul*, *Golden Boy* and *Run With The Wind*? **Boxing**

8. True or false: in 1996 there were more than 100 casinos in the UK? **True**

9. What is a fidibus? **A paper match or spill**

10. Of which African country is Lubumbashi the main mining town? **Zaire**

11. What is Punic faith? **Treachery**

12. In which sport were Harry Lancaster, Quentin Berriman and James Williams all British champions? **Fencing**

13. Who appeared in the TV series *Callan*, *Target* and *Special Branch*? **Patrick Mower**

14. Which heroine, in the Apocrypha, killed Holofernes?
Judith

15. Which opera has characters called Fiordiligi, Dorabella, Despina and Ferrando? *Cosi Fan Tutte*

16. What was the real name of the literary hero variously called Hawkeye, Leatherstocking and Deerslayer?
Natty Bumppo

17. Would you find a futchel: in a horse-drawn carriage, in a mill or in a steam-engine? **In a horse-drawn carriage**

18. Who had a 1974 No 1 hit with *Ms Grace*? **Tymes**

19. Of whom did Bismarck say: "Der alte Jude, das ist ein Mann."? **Disraeli**

20. What sort of creature is a tamma? **A wallaby**

21. Who starred in the films *Dark Victory*, *A Stolen Life*, *Another Man's Poison* and *The Nanny*? **Bette Davis**

22. In which country is the city of Oldenburg: USA, Germany or Switzerland? **Germany**

23. Which season ends at the vernal equinox? **Winter**

24. What appears in the third quarter of the Royal Arms?
A harp

25. In which sport was Suncrest Sail a 1996 champion?
Greyhound racing

26. Name the actress mother of actress Joely Richardson.
Vanessa Redgrave

27. Which comedian played the title role in the TV drama *Deacon Brodie*? **Billy Connolly**

28. In euchre, which cards are known as the right and left bowers? **The Jacks**

29. In which year did Prince Philip become a British subject?
1947

30. In which ocean is the Java Trench? **Indian Ocean**

31. Which American hero has been played in films by Joel McCrea, Charlton Heston, Louis Calhern and Paul Newman? **Buffalo Bill**

32. Who had three successive No 1 hits from 1988 to 1989 and then reached No 5 with *Every Day*? **Jason Donovan**

33. With what does Seaby's Standard Catalogue deal?
British coins

34. Which race were immortal in *Gulliver's Travels*?
The Struldbrugs

35. Which word means to throw, a cut of beef and a bit-holding device? **Chuck**

36. Who played DCI Tom Barnaby in the TV series *Midsomer Murders*? **John Nettles**

37. What name is given to the three days preceding Ascension Day? **Rogation Days**

38. In which country is the Dasht-e Lut desert? **Iran**

39. Who was the father of King John? **Henry II**

40. What name is given to medieval dramatic representations based on sacred history of legends of the saints?
Miracle plays

41. Whose Top Ten hits included *Red Dress, You You You* and *Pretend*? **Alvin Stardust**

42. Who wrote *The Long Banana Skin* and *A Shy Person's Guide To Life*? **Michael Bentine**

43. Which tennis champion partnered Petr Korda to win the Australian Open Men's Doubles in 1996? **Stefan Edberg**

44. Name the actress daughter of actress Maureen O'Sullivan.
Mia Farrow

45. Which country has the largest number of merchant ships: Japan, Liberia or Panama? **Japan**

46. What was the name of the cloned sheep which attracted media attention in 1997? **Dolly**

47. Who, in the USA, does lemon law protect?
Buyers of faulty cars

48. True or false: Argentina won more gold medals than the UK in the 1996 Olympics?
False (They won none – Britain won one)

49. In which sport did England play four Test Matches against the Cook Islands in 1995? **Netball**

50. Who played Michael in the TV series *Loved By You*?
John Gordon Sinclair

51. Who had Top Twenty hits with *Tramp, Hard To Handle* and *My Girl*? **Otis Redding**

52. Who or what carries out a demivolte?
A horse (it is a way of raising its legs)

53. Who is next in the Order of Precedence after the Sovereign's cousins? **Archbishop of Canterbury**

54. Which actress, wife of Clark Gable, died in a plane crash?
Carole Lombard

55. Which of these animals is not protected by the Wildlife and Countryside Act: hare, red squirrel or leech? **Hare**

56. Who wrote the satirical poem *The Dunciad*?
Alexander Pope

57. Where are the Elcho, Albert, Hopton Challenge Cup and Kolapore Cup all contested? **Bisley**

58. Which word means a backless seat, an embroidery frame and a needle-case? **Tabouret**

59. What does an emphractic medicine do?
Closes the pores of the skin

60. What were the names of the middle-aged sweethearts in the TV series *As Time Goes By*? **Jean and Lionel**

61. At which famous battle did Miltiades command the winning army? **Marathon**

62. Who live in a zenana? **Muslim or Hindu women**

63. Which surname was shared by pop singers Jo Ann, Junior, Tevin and Pat? **Campbell**

64. Which composer has been played in films by Stephen Haggard, Oskar Werner and Tom Hulce? **Mozart**

65. In which county are Hailes Abbey, Sudeley Castle and Berkeley Castle? **Gloucestershire**

66. Where would you find a flash-board? **In a mill course**

67. Whose Top Twenty hits included *Give Me the Night, Love X Love* and *In Your Eyes*? **George Benson**

68. What is formed by a taliacotian operation? **A new nose**

69. In Judaism where would you find the Mishnah and the Gemara? **In the Talmud**

70. How many individual events comprise Men's Olympic gymnastics? **6**

71. Is a stolon a stonemason's tool, a trailing shoot or a wild pigeon? **A trailing shoot**

72. Which literary character was persuaded to stop acting foolishly by Samson Carrasco? **Don Quixote**

73. After Julius Caesar's death, who formed the triumvirate with Mark Antony and Octavian? **Marcus Lepidus**

74. Who had a No 1 hit with *Jack Your Body*?
Steve 'Silk' Hurley

75. What is reeled in a filature? **Silk**

76. Which English town was known as Danum to the Romans? **Doncaster**

77. At which London hotel were the Orpheans and Havana bands renowned in the 1920s? **The Savoy Hotel**

78. Was a gebur a tenant farmer, a woollen cloak or a cooking-pot? **A tenant farmer**

79. Which film star died after filming a fight scene in the film *Solomon and Sheba*? **Tyrone Power**

80. In German towns, what is the Rathaus? **The town-hall**

81. In the TV series *M*A*S*H* what was Trapper John's surname? **McIntyre**

82. Where is John Moores University? **Liverpool**

83. In which islands is the Sound of Harris?
Outer Hebrides (Western Isles)

84. Is purslane a form of lace, a medical condition or a herb?
A herb

85. What were the Commonwealth Games originally called?
British Empire Games

86. What nationality was world chess champion José Capablanca? **Cuban**

87. Who had a Top Ten hit in 1977 with *Have I the Right*?
Dead End Kids

88. Which sea has Borneo to the west, the Sulu Archipelago to the north and Sulawesi to the south? **Celebes Sea**

89. Which of these is not a London Borough Council: Enfield, Merton or Bloomsbury? **Bloomsbury**

90. True or false: the composer Brahms was married five times? **False (He never married)**

91. Which film star said: "If I had my career over again? Maybe I'd say to myself, speed it up a little."? **James Stewart**

92. In which Thomas Hardy novel does Damon Wildeve marry Thomasin Yeobright? *The Return of the Native*

93. Who, on TV, regularly referred to Captain Mainwaring and his men as "Ruddy hooligans!"? **Chief Warden Hodges**

94. Which city was to have been the venue for the 1940 Olympics? **Tokyo**

95. What is a ringhals or rinkhals? **A poisonous snake**

96. Which word means a small child, something usable salvaged from a dustbin etc and to add (up)? **Tot**

97. Is a whimbrel a curiosity, a bird or a garment? **A bird**

98. In which 1982 film was Steve Martin 'shot' by Alan Ladd, James Cagney and William Conrad? *Dead Men Don't Wear Plaid*

99. On which river does St Albans stand? **River Ver**

100. Which country won most boxing gold medals in the 1996 Olympics? **Cuba (4)**

Quiz 3

1. Who was the first president of an independent Texas?

    Sam Houston

2. Who played Grand Vizier Jaffar in the 1940 film *The Thief of Bagdad*? **Conrad Veidt**

3. Which stretch of water lies between Duncansby Head and South Ronaldsway? **Pentland Firth**

4. To which fish family does the anchovy belong? **Herring**

5. Is an anchorite a novice, a shell-fish or a recluse?

    A recluse

6. Which English king died of dysentery at Vincennes in 1422? **Henry V**

7. Whose only No 1 hit was *Love Grows (Where My Rosemary Goes)*? **Edison Lighthouse**

8. What colour dye is produced by arsenic sulphide or orpiment? **Yellow**

9. Which English city was the setting for the TV drama series *The Grand*? **Manchester**

10. Which team sold Babe Ruth to the New York Yankees in 1921? **Boston Red Sox**

11. What would you be doing in Saxon times if you said "Wacht heil"?

    Drinking someone's health or making a toast

12. Which monarch corresponded with the Duchess of Marlborough using the name Mrs Morley? **Queen Anne**

13. Is bombazine a dessert, a dress material or a type of quartz? **Dress material**

14. Who played Mama Rose in the 1993 remake of the film *Gypsy*? **Bette Midler**

15. Who married Edward Borough, Lord Latimer, an English king and Thomas Seymour? **Catherine Parr**

16. Which county side were captained by David Boon in the 1997 cricket season? **Durham**

17. Which magical TV character was born in 64 BC in Baghdad? **Jeannie (in *I Dream Of Jeannie*)**

18. In which TV series did Claire Bloom play Frances Pye? ***Family Money***

19. Who had Top Ten hits with *Get the Message* and *Disappointed*? **Electronic**

20. Which world leader did Giuseppi Zangara attempt to assassinate in 1933? **F D Roosevelt**

21. Which war did Rip Van Winkle sleep through? **American War of Independence**

22. In what capacity did John Tradescant work for Charles I? **Gardener**

23. True or false: 'Fine-Hair', 'Greycloak' and 'Blood-axe' were nicknames of Kings of Denmark? **False (Norway)**

24. Naturalist Ludwig Koch was a pioneer in what? **Recording bird and animal sounds**

25. What was the name of 'The Lord of the Rings'? **Sauron the Great**

26. Which US State is known both as the Old Line State and the Free State? **Maryland**

27. Who wore an M B waistcoat: members of the clergy, waiters or footmen? **Members of the clergy**

28. Which stage show sprang out of the *Riverdance* stage show? ***Lord of the Dance***

29. With which British city is 'Beau' Nash associated? **Bath**

30. Who played Joe Wicks in TV's *Eastenders*?

Paul Nicholls

31. Who played the alien in the film *My Stepmother Is An Alien*?

Kim Basinger

32. Who had a 1986 No 1 called *The Final Countdown*?

Europe

33. Who was the first black footballer to captain England?

Paul Ince

34. Is trine a religious term, an astrological expression or a form of architecture?

An astrological expression

35. Of what is a joule a unit?

Energy

36. What is sold in a white sale?

Household linen

37. Which trees are called linden by the Germans?

Lime trees

38. Who was the hero in the TV serial *The Monster of Peladon*?

Dr Who

39. Which fashion-designer opened The Fulham Road Clothes Shop and showed her first dress collection in 1969?

Zandra Rhodes

40. Which poet wrote *Enoch Arden* and *Rizpah*?

Tennyson

41. In what field are marks of cadency used?

Heraldry

42. Was 'Buster' Keaton's first name Joseph, Herbert or Michael?

Joseph

43. Which is the largest island between Corsica and Italy?

Elba

44. Which legendary king had a horse called Lamri?

King Arthur

45. Where is the Pitti art gallery?

Florence

46. Which one word can mean an ornamental pattern, to worry and a bar on a musical instrument? **Fret**

47. Who directed the film *Truly Madly Deeply*?
Anthony Minghella

48. On TV, who were Po, Dipsy, Tinky Winky and Laa Laa?
The Teletubbies

49. Which poet used what he called 'sprung rhythm'?
Gerard Manley Hopkins

50. Who had Top Twenty hits with *Love Train*, *Americanos* and *Ferry 'Cross the Mersey*? **Holly Johnson**

51. Who gave the order for the scuttling of the German fleet at Scapa Flow in 1919? **Admiral Ludwig von Reuter**

52. Which football club, comprising Oxford and Cambridge University players, won the F A Amateur Cup in 1953?
Pegasus

53. Which French commander said at Verdun: "They shall not pass"? **Henri Pétain**

54. Is bouclé a form of painting, the perfume of a wine or a yarn? **A yarn**

55. Which poetess wrote the novels *Novel On Yellow Paper*, *Over the Frontier* and *The Holiday*? **Stevie Smith**

56. For what were Harry Jenkins, Thomas Parr and Ada Roe renowned? **Extreme old age**

57. Of what were the Standing Fishes, Wife-hater, Sting and Goose all forms? **Bibles**

58. What is the name of the streamlined structure added to motor-cycles, ships and aircraft? **Fairing**

59. True or false: Conductor André Previn was born in Paris?
False (Berlin)

60. Where does marram grass usually grow?
On sand dunes, at the seashore

61. The 1963 film *Death Drums Along the River* was an update of which 1935 film? **Sanders of the River**

62. Who had Top Ten hits with *It Keep Rainin'*, *Here I Stand* and *Dedicated To the One I Love*? **Bitty Mclean**

63. In cloth terms, if Lincoln was green and Coventry was blue, what colour was Yorkshire? **Grey**

64. Who played Frank Tate in TV's *Emmerdale*?
Norman Bowler

65. Which bird is also called an apteryx? **Kiwi**

66. Who built the steamship *Clermont* in 1807?
Robert Fulton

67. What nationality was the first man to run 100 metres in 10 seconds? **German (Armin Hary)**

68. Is a dorado an inscribed ring, a fish or a rounded column?
A fish

69. Ashdod, Netanya, Akko and Palmahim are all on the coast of which country? **Israel**

70. Who wrote the plays *The Ruffian on the Stair*, *The Erpingham Camp* and *What the Butler Saw*? **Joe Orton**

71. In Greek legend, where did the Hyperboreans dwell?
Beyond the North Wind

72. In 1917 what was nicknamed the Packet of Woodbines: a ship, a fort or a tank?. **A ship (which had five funnels)**

73. Who played George Raft in the film *The George Raft Story*? **Ray Danton**

74. What official position was held by Lady Emma Hamilton's husband? **British Ambassador**

75. Who had a 1984 No 1 with *I Want To Know What Love Is*? **Foreigner**

76. Is a cabriole a horse-drawn carriage, a vegetable or a style of furniture leg? **A style of furniture leg**

77. In which country is Rupert's (or Prince Rupert's) Land? **Canada**

78. What is the official residence of the Lord Mayor of London? **Mansion House**

79. Who was the first presenter of the adult version of TV's *Blockbusters*? **Michael Aspel**

80. Is chervil a herb, a type of fine leather or a sedimentary rock? **A herb**

81. Which woman tennis player reached the finals of the Australian, French and US Singles in 1966 – and won none of them? **Nancy Richey**

82. Under what name did Charles Hamilton achieve fame as a writer? **Frank Richards**

83. Who composed *Manon Lescaut*, *Le Villi* and *Edgar*? **Puccini**

84. Which word means an impetuous attack, custody and a heraldic device? **Charge**

85. What was the nickname of New Zealand Prime Minister Richard Seddon? **King Dick**

86. Traditionally, which bird plucked a thorn out of Christ's crown on the way to Calvary? **Robin**

87. Who played the female lead in the film *The English Patient*? **Kirstin Scott Thomas**

88. When did the Gas Light and Coke Company come into being in Britain: 1810, 1830 or 1860? **1810**

89. Whose last Top Ten hit was *Soley Soley*?

Middle of the Road

90. What was the setting for the TV series *The Kingdom*?

A hospital

91. Who was Abraham Lincoln's Vice President?

Andrew Johnson

92. Which country did Kipling refer to as 'Our Lady of the Snows': Tibet, Canada or Nepal? **Canada**

93. Who was the first Olympic gymnast to achieve a perfect score? **Nadia Comaneci**

94. Where is the Northumberland Strait? **Canada**

95. Prince of the Asturias was a traditional title for the heir to which throne? **Spain's**

96. What was the nickname of the Royal East Kent Regiment?

The Buffs

97. Which TV series featured the characters Commander Sisko, Major Nerys and Chief O'Brien?

Star Trek – Deep Space Nine

98. Who played the title role in the 1960 film *Pollyanna*?

Hayley Mills

99. Would you find a foliot on a shield, in a fort or in a clock? **In a clock**

100. True or false: 'The Galloping Ghost' was a US football player? **True (Red Grange)**

Quiz 4

1. Whose Top Twenty hits included *1-2-3 O'Leary*, *The Tips of My Fingers* and *Loneliness*? **Des O'Connor's**

2. In Japan is a kakemono a garment, a wall-picture or a type of theatre? **Wall-picture**

3. Who led the Visigoths when they sacked Rome in 410 AD? **Alaric**

4. What do bobbers do? **Unload trawlers**

5. Which was the first country to win the Football World Cup in successive tournaments? **Italy**

6. Which singer is associated with *Maybellene*, *School Days* and *Johnny B Goode*? **Chuck Berry**

7. Who wrote *The Millstones*, *The Middle Ground* and *The Radiant Way*? **Margaret Drabble**

8. Which Wimbledon tennis champion acted in the film *The Horse Soldiers*? **Althea Gibson**

9. Who would use an écraseur: a sculptor, a surgeon or an artist? **A surgeon**

10. Who had Top Ten hits with *Secret Lovers* and *Always*? **Atlantic Starr**

11. Who played Smiler in TV's *Last of the Summer Wine*? **Stephen Lewis**

12. True or false: Gavrilo Princip, assassin of Archduke Franz Ferdinand, was never executed? **True**

13. Is framboesia an orchid, a dessert or a tropical disease? **Tropical disease (Yaws)**

14. What are Mongefossen, Boyoma and Tugela? **Waterfalls**

15. Which country gave the Hebrides to Scotland in 1266? **Norway**

16. In which country is the kip the unit of currency? **Laos**

17. Which word can go before cheeked, jack, cart and dumpling? **Apple**

18. Who composed *Duke Bluebeard's Castle*, *The Wooden Prince* and *The Miraculous Mandarin*? **Béla Bartok**

19. Name one of the actors who played the title roles in the film *The Two Jakes*? **Jack Nicholson or Harvey Keitel**

20. Who had Top Ten hits with *Cornflake Girl* and *Pretty Good Year*? **Tori Amos**

21. Who from 1949 to 1974 compiled a 46 volume guide to interesting British buildings? **Nikolaus Pevsner**

22. What nationality was TV 'singer' Margarita Pracatan? **Cuban**

23. Who was on the back of the £50 note issued in 1994? **Sir John Houblon**

24. Is a fanon a cut of pork, a napkin used during a Catholic Mass or a hair-slide? **A napkin used during Mass**

25. Which Greek philosopher's followers were known as 'peripatetics'? **Aristotle's**

26. Which famous novelist and poet illustrated many of Hilaire Belloc's books? **G K Chesterton**

27. Who chose the gold casket in *The Merchant of Venice*? **Prince of Morocco**

28. For what is babbit's metal used? **To reduce friction**

29. Who would use a bason in his or her work? **A hat-maker**

30. Which animals are affected by the condition known as stag-evil? **Horses (It is lockjaw)**

31. The first King George VI and Queen Elizabeth Stakes was run to mark which event? **The Festival of Britain**

32. Who won the Oscar for Best Director for the film *Ordinary People*? **Robert Redford**

33. Is a trochil a flower, a bird or a poetic metre? **A bird**

34. Which children's TV series had characters called Roger Bones, Lambkin Bones, Captain Bullock and Gran? ***Pirates***

35. Which King of England married Caroline of Anspach? **George II**

36. Which republic is near Rimini on the Adriatic? **San Marino**

37. Under what name did the Earl of Guildford serve as Prime Minister? **Lord North**

38. What is the Masoretic Text? **A version of the Old Testament**

39. Who had a 1990 No 1 hit with *Killer*? **Adamski**

40. What is the gauge of British railway lines? **4 ft 8½ inches**

41. True or false: the Suez Canal has no locks? **True**

42. For what is the gas butadiene used? **Making synthetic rubber**

43. Which Irish poet won the 1995 Nobel Prize for Literature? **Seamus Heaney**

44. Who won the British Open Golf championship for the third year in succession in 1956? **Peter Thomson**

45. Which English king was fatally wounded at Châluz? **Richard I**

46. Who played the US President in the film *The Pelican Brief*? **Robert Culp**

47. In monetary terms, how much is a monkey? **£500**

48. Who wrote *The New Girl at St Chad's*, *A Fourth Form Friendship* and *Captain Peggie*? **Angela Brazil**

49. Who founded Habitat? **Terence Conran**

50. What does granodising prevent: metal corrosion, wine fermentation or moulting in chickens? **Metal corrosion**

51. Which dish is made by curdling cream with wine, adding flavouring and frothing it up? **Syllabub**

52. Which singing group comprised Bill Kenny, Charlie Fuqua, Hoppy Jones and Deek Watson? **The Ink Spots**

53. Where would you die if you died a 'strae' death? **In bed**

54. Who had a No 1 hit with *Float On* in 1977? **Floaters**

55. In which TV series did twins David and Tony Webb play twins Stanley and Bruce Matthews? ***Hi-de-Hi!***

56. Who, in films, played Zorro, Jesse James, Eddie Duchin and Ferdinand de Lesseps? **Tyrone Power**

57. Who owned the Spyglass Inn in *Treasure Island*? **Long John Silver**

58. Who succeeded Don Revie as manager of the England football team? **Ron Greenwood**

59. Who incurred the monarch's displeasure by a secret marriage to Elizabeth Throckmorton? **Walter Raleigh**

60. Of whom is Keats speaking when he says: "whoever seeks abroad may find/Thee sitting careless on a granary floor"? **Autumn**

61. In what field was William Fox Talbot an influential pioneer? **Photography**

62. Is a querquedule a lizard, a duck or a pig? **A duck**

63. What do Compostela, Walsingham and Tours have in common? **Sites for pilgrimages**

64. Which tissue forms the central part or medulla of the stems of plants? **Pith**

65. Who wrote *The Narrative of Arthur Gordon Pym* and *Tamerlane and Other Poems*? **Edgar Allan Poe**

66. Which adjective means 'having a changeable lustre or colour, like a cat's eye in the dark': feluminine, metachromatic or chatoyant? **Chatoyant**

67. Which member of the trio at the start of the Potsdam Conference in 1945 was later replaced? **Winston Churchill**

68. Which American mammal is known as the 'washing bear'? **Racoon (It washes its food)**

69. Which bird is sometimes called the snow-grouse? **Ptarmigan**

70. True or false: Ceòl Beag and Ceòl Mar are Highland bagpipe music? **True**

71. Who became the first West Indian to play cricket for England against the West Indies when he played in Bridgetown in 1981? **Roland Butcher**

72. Who painted *Family of Saltimbanques* and *Les Demoiselles d'Avignon*? **Picasso**

73. In which language was the play *Six Characters in Search of an Author* originally written? **Italian**

74. Which is the smallest planet? **Pluto**

75. What usually 'maderizes'? **White wine (It loses colour and taste)**

76. Golden, grey, ringed and dotterel are all species of which bird? **Plover**

77. In legal theory, who governs Britain from when a
government resigns until a new government is appointed?
The Privy Council

78. Give the surname of the TV family in *2 Point 4 Children*.
Porter

79. Who composed the operas *The Spanish Hour* and *The
Child of the Spells*? **Ravel**

80. Who was England's first £100 a week footballer?
Johnny Haynes

81. Which famous writer was pilloried for writing *The
Shortest Way With Dissenters*? **Daniel Defoe**

82. Which European country's playing cards traditionally had
acorn, leaf, bell and heart as the four suits? **Germany**

83. In which country is Cape York Peninsula? **Australia**

84. Which people's god was represented as a plumed serpent?
The Aztecs'

85. *Dream Warriors*, *Dream Master* and *Dream Child* were
all sequels to which film? ***A Nightmare On Elm Street***

86. What is measured (in volume) by a Hoppus foot?
Timber

87. What was the stage name of singer Edith Giovanna
Gassion? **Edith Piaf**

88. Against which team did Richard Hadlee take his 400th
Test wicket? **India**

89. What became the first artificial 'planet' when it went into
orbit round the sun in 1959? **Lunik I**

90. Who was the first American Postmaster General?
Benjamin Franklin

91. Which composer and organist was buried at the foot of the organ in Westminster Abbey in 1695? **Henry Purcell**

92. Which Pulitzer Prize-winning novel by E A Proux was set in Newfoundland? ***The Shipping News***

93. Who had Top Ten hits with *The Key The Secret* and *Feels Like Heaven*? **Urban Cookie Collective**

94. In athletics who was the first man in any event to hold simultaneously the Olympic, World and Commonwealth titles and World record? **Daley Thompson**

95. What kind of fruit is a mazard? **A cherry**

96. What was patented in 1824 by L W Wright: a pin-making machine, flanged locomotive wheels or a talking doll?
A pin-making machine

97. If a circle is divided by two perpendicular diameters, what are the parts called? **Quadrants**

98. Who was the central character of the TV series *Crocodile Shoes*? **Jed Shepperd**

99. In which sport does a conveyor liberate? **Pigeon-racing**

100. By what name is the Gilbert and Sullivan operetta *Bunthorne's Bride* better known? ***Patience***

Quiz 5

1. Who had Top Ten hits with *Young Parisians*, *Dog Eat Dog* and *Friend Or Foe*? **Adam Ant**

2. Of which people was Atahualpa the last ruler?
The Incas

3. In the game of whist, what term means holding the first and third best cards of a suit? **Tenace**

4. In *Coronation Street*, who set fire to Mike Baldwin's factory? **Don Brennan**

5. Which word means clever, chief and a curve? **Arch**

6. Who would use a dochmius, a spondee and an anapaest? **A poet**

7. Is a harp-seal a seal, a hallmark or a type of solder? **A seal**

8. Which Canadian province has cities called Moose Jaw, Prince Albert and Yorkton? **Saskatchewan**

9. Which country was the setting for the film *Burnt By the Sun*? **Russia**

10. Is an entellus a monkey, a bone fracture or a flint artefact? **A monkey**

11. Where would you find a balistraria? **In a castle wall (It is a loophole)**

12. Who wrote *Riders* and *Appassionata*? **Jilly Cooper**

13. What kind of animal was the TV cartoon character Rocko? **A wallaby**

14. In which English city is Cartwright Hall, St George's Hall, Bolling Hall and The Wool Exchange? **Bradford**

15. Whose jazz band's only Top Ten hit was *Petite Fleur*? **Chris Barber's**

16. Which TV character lived at 127 Inkerman Terrace? **Terry Collier**

17. Which great film star, son of a marine biologist, worked as a shipping-clerk, tobacco-plantation manager and gold hunter before breaking into films? **Errol Flynn**

18. Who suffer from byssinosis? **Cotton-workers**

19. In which town is the University of Hertfordshire situated?
Hatfield

20. Is dornick a cloth, a runic alphabet or a block of stone?
A cloth

21. In law, what is a feme sole?   **An unmarried woman**

22. Which breed of dog is known as 'the barkless dog'?
Basenji

23. In brewing, what is a spile?   **A bung**

24. Who played chauffeur Thomas Watkins in TV's *Upstairs Downstairs*?   **John Alderton**

25. Of which country are the Juan Fernandez Islands and Easter Island possessions?   **Chile**

26. Who played game warden Robert Payton in the films *West of Zanzibar* and *Where No Vultures Fly*?   **Anthony Steel**

27. Who wrote *Watteau, The Genius of the Future* and *Friends From England*?   **Anita Brookner**

28. Who abdicated as Queen of the Netherlands in 1948?
Queen Wilhemina

29. Which European country's king died in 1920 as a result of a monkey bite?   **Greece's**

30. Whose Top Twenty hits included *No Sleep Till Brooklyn*, *She's On It* and *Get It Together*?   **Beastie Boys**

31. What is a dry-pile?   **A voltaic battery**

32. On which creature would you find calipash and calipee?
A turtle

33. Who played TV detective Adam Dalgleish?
Roy Marsden

34. Who flew in an aircraft called *Jason*?   **Amy Johnson**

35. Who wrote *Grantchester Grind*? **Tom Sharpe**

36. In how many values is Maundy Money minted? **Four**

37. True or false: the Thames Barrier has 12 rising gates?
False (10)

38. In the UK, what are Belmont, Beneficial, Carter Allen
Ltd, Habibsons and Riggs AP? **Banks**

39. Which English cricketer scored his 21st Test century in
his 100th Test Match in 1968? **Colin Cowdrey**

40. Who won Best Actress Oscar for her role in *Fargo* in
1997? **Frances McDormand**

41. Which member of The Goodies presented birdwatching
programmes on TV? **Bill Oddie**

42. Who commanded the BEF in France in 1914 until
succeeded by Haig? **John French**

43. Which word can go before grand, carriage, minder and
walker? **Baby**

44. Is spelt a soldering alloy, a type of wheat or quartz?
A type of wheat

45. Who was editor of *The Times* from 1967 to 1981?
William Rees-Mogg

46. Who graduated from West Point in 1861 34th out of a
class of 34? **George A Custer**

47. Who had Top Twenty hits with *Fields of Fire, Chance*
and *Look Away*? **Big Country**

48. Whom did Muhammad Ali beat when he won the World
Title for the third time? **Leon Spinks**

49. Which religious group issued a religious paper called *The
Middle Way*? **The Buddhist Society**

50. Which one word can mean to colonize, a long seat and to sink to the bottom? **Settle**

51. True or false: The Platters' only No 1 hit in the UK was *The Great Pretender*?
False (It was *Smoke Gets In Your Eyes*)

52. Who played The Pope in the film *The Shoes of the Fisherman*? **Anthony Quinn**

53. Methomania is a longing for order, a desire to measure objects or a craving for intoxicating drink?
A craving for intoxicating drink

54. Which 'pistol' is used to fire flares and signal rockets?
A Very pistol

55. Which Greek biographer's *Lives* provided Shakespeare with the details of his classical plays? **Plutarch**

56. In which US state would you be if you sailed down the Seekonk River into Narragansett Bay? **Rhode Island**

57. Which Hitchcock film had the publicity line: "If a woman answers – hang on for dear life"? *Dial M For Murder*

58. What was the only Top Ten hit for the Flowerpot Men?
Let's Go To San Francisco

59. For what was Eustace the Monk infamous in the 13th century? **He was a pirate!**

60. Which boxer lost his World Heavyweight Title in 1964 when he stayed on his stool at the end of the sixth round?
Sonny Liston

61. Which flower has traditionally been the symbol of sleep and the dead? **Poppy**

62. Who had collections of poetry called *The Colossus* and *Ariel*? **Sylvia Plath**

63. On TV who was the Gamesmaster? **Patrick Moore**

64. In literature, who was the Modern Prometheus?
Frankenstein

65. Whom did Richard Gere hire as his companion in *Pretty Woman*?
Julia Roberts

66. Who had a No 1 hit in 1983 with *Only You*?
Flying Pickets

67. Which musical instrument was invented by Bartolomeo Cristofori?
Pianoforte

68. Which country first introduced the potato into Europe?
Spain

69. What is a lasque: an old corset, a diamond or part of a suit of armour?
Diamond

70. Of which modern musical instrument was the chalumeau a forerunner?
The clarinet

71. Which fish is nicknamed Lord of the Stream and King of the Lake?
Pike

72. What was the name of the school founded by Plato in 387 BC?
The Academy

73. In which US city is there a frogless pond called The Frog Pond: Boston, Chicago or Albany?
Boston

74. If you are riant, are you cheerful, miserable, rich or poor?
Cheerful

75. Who was the famous teacher of Helen Keller?
Anne Sullivan

76. Which was the last *Road* film?
Road To Hong Kong

77. What magical object did Harmony Parker possess in the TV series *The Queen's Nose*?
A 50 pence coin

78. What edible object do you need to play the game philopena?
A nut

79. Which country played in seven successive Davis Cup Finals until 1989? **Sweden**

80. Which historical character did John Wayne portray in the film *The Conqueror*? **Genghis Khan**

81. Which author recounted his World War I experiences in the books *Gallipoli Memories, Athenian Memories* and *Greek Memories*? **Compton Mackenzie**

82. Who scored all the goals when England beat Cyprus 5-0 in a 1975 football match? **Malcolm MacDonald**

83. Whose Top Ten hits included *I've Been Losing You, Cry Wolf* and *Stay On These Roads*? **A-Ha**

84. Which word means the highest part of the road, a size of paper and a coin? **Crown**

85. Which country made the TV series *The Water Margin*? **Japan**

86. Which tree had the nicknames hen-drunks and cock-drunks because it was thought that fowls became intoxicated if they fed on its berries? **Rowan (Mountain Ash)**

87. In the Laurel and Hardy film *Angora Love* what was Angora Love? **A goat**

88. True or false: British troops tried to capture Buenos Aires in 1807? **True**

89. On which island is the world's largest deposit of asphalt? **Trinidad**

90. What did Melanion use to defeat Atalanta in a foot race? **Golden apples**

91. Who said: ''Wives are young men's mistresses; companions in middle age; and old men's nurses.''? **Francis Bacon**

92. Who wrote the books *H M Corvette*, *East Coast Corvette* and *Corvette Command*?   **Nicholas Monsarrat**

93. Who had a 1990 No 1 hit with *A Little Time*?
                                                The Beautiful South

94. On which island did John have the vision that he recounts in the Book of Revelation?   **Patmos**

95. Which England Test Cricket captain said, before a visit by the West Indians, "We will make them grovel."?
                                                Tony Greig

96. Who played the title role in the film *Meet Danny Wilson*?
                                                Frank Sinatra

97. Name the subject of the TV series *The O Zone*.   **Music**

98. In mythology, in which land was the Golden Fleece?
                                                Colchis

99. Where is Logan Airport?   **Boston**

100. According to tradition, who had the Uffington White Horse cut?   **King Alfred**

Quiz 6

1.   Who travelled with Steve Martin in the film *Planes, Trains and Automobiles*?   **John Candy**

2.   Which is the most famous piece of music in the opera *The Tale of Tsar Saltan*?   ***The Flight of the Bumble Bee***

3.   Which tree is also called hen-apple, sea owler, hoar withy, Cumberland hawthorn and whipcrop?   **White Beam**

4.   In literature, what was the name of the captain created by C J Cutcliffe Hyne?   **Kettle**

5.   Which river formed the Grand Canyon?   **Colorado River**

6. From which plant is the tonic substance cynarine obtained? **Globe artichoke**

7. What relation was Leopold I of Belgium to Queen Victoria? **Uncle**

8. At what time does the second dog watch begin on a ship? **6 pm**

9. Which one word means a herb of the cabbage family, a firework and a telling-off? **Rocket**

10. Who partnered Julio Iglesias on the Top Ten hit *All Of You*? **Diana Ross**

11. Is Kol Nidre a huge crater in Siberia, a geyser in Iceland or a Jewish service? **A Jewish service**

12. In the film *The Accidental Tourist* what was Geena Davis's job? **A dog-trainer**

13. Name the opposing captain to John Parrott on TV's *A Question of Sport*. **Ally McCoist**

14. Who composed *Careless Rapture* and *Perchance To Dream*? **Ivor Novello**

15. Which artist, who painted many self-portraits, often used his son Titus as his model? **Rembrandt**

16. In a measured trial held in Perth, Australia, in 1979, who was recorded as the world's fastest bowler? **Jeff Thomson**

17. Which type of musical composition is said to have been inspired by the songs of the Venetian gondoliers? **The Barcarolle (or Barcarole)**

18. In Virginia Woolf's fantasy *Orlando*, what happened to Orlando when he woke from his seven day trance? **He had become a woman**

19. What does an omophagic creature eat? **Raw meat**

20. What would you be doing if you used a lazy-daisy?
Embroidery (It is a stitch)

21. Who did George C Scott think he was in the film *They Might Be Giants*? **Sherlock Holmes**

22. Which trio voiced the animated series *Bananaman*?
The Goodies

23. True or false: St Francis was the first Christian monk?
False (St Anthony was)

24. Which was the world's first nuclear-powered merchant vessel? **USS *Savannah***

25. If you were an expert in morbidezza, what would you do for a living? **Paint (It is expert flesh tinting)**

26. Who recorded *N-N-Nineteen Not Out* in 1985 as The Commentators? **Rory Bremner**

27. What name is given to the rearmost mast on a three-masted ship? **Mizzenmast**

28. Who, in 1990, became only the second person to run a sub-four-minute mile at Iffley Road running track in Oxford? **Simon Mugglestone**

29. Which most religious Jewish relic was lost when the Babylonians destroyed Jerusalem in 586 BC?
The Ark of the Covenant

30. Which word means the ability to escape capture (or death) by separating and abandoning the part of the body gripped by an enemy: autotomy, autoschism or autolysis?
Autotomy

31. Name the subject of the TV series presented by Stefan Buczacki. **Gardening**

32. Which French city, on the bank of the River Vesle, has The Gate of Mars and is the centre of the champagne region? **Rheims**

33. Who played the young Indiana Jones in the film *Indiana Jones and the Last Crusade*? **River Phoenix**

34. Which was the first public museum in Britain? **Ashmolean Museum**

35. In mythology, which brother of Prometheus led a revolt against Zeus? **Atlas**

36. To what does the adjective 'halieutic' refer? **Fishing**

37. Who wrote the novels *Dragonwyck, Foxfire, Devil Water* and *Green Darkness*? **Anya Seton**

38. What did George III's 'table-deckers' use to decorate the dinner table at Windsor? **Coloured sand**

39. Which bird is sometimes called the merle by poets? **Blackbird**

40. In which county are the Clent Hills? **Worcestershire**

41. Who had Top Ten hits with *Tell It To My Heart* and *Prove Your Love*? **Taylor Dayne**

42. What is a fatiloquist? **A fortune-teller**

43. How many Asian peaks are more than 24,000 feet in height: 72, 83 or 94? **94**

44. Which two colours are usually confused in Daltonism? **Red and green**

45. Dutch Purple is a variety of which culinary plant? **Asparagus**

46. Of which mining concern did Cecil Rhodes become chairman in 1889? **De Beers**

47. Which of these countries is *not* landlocked: Belarus, Gabon, Burundi or Armenia? **Gabon**

48. How old was Jennifer Capriati when she made her professional tennis debut? **13**

49. What is the name of the Swedish Parliament? **The Riksdag**

50. Who wrote the sea-stories *Peter Simple* and *Mr Midshipman Easy*? **Frederick Marryat**

51. Which helpful organisation did Clara Barton found in the USA? **American Red Cross**

52. Which word means a blind alley, intimate, near together and warm and damp? **Close**

53. Which composer's music is usually performed in the festival theatre in Bayreuth? **Wagner's**

54. Who defeated Theodore Roosevelt in the 1912 US Presidential election? **Woodrow Wilson**

55. Which record did Doctor and the Medics take to No 1 in 1986? ***Spirit in the Sky***

56. True or false: dancette is a term used in architecture and heraldry? **True**

57. In which film did Groucho Marx become Prime Minister of Fredonia? ***Duck Soup***

58. On 20 October 1990 the match between Manchester United and Arsenal degenerated into a brawl involving 21 of the players: which player was not involved? **David Seaman**

59. Whose only Top Ten hits were *Swingin' Shepherd Blues* and *Mack the Knife*? **Ella Fitzgerald**

60. With what does hamartiology deal: bathing, sin or massage? **Sin**

61. Which golfer said: "Seve hits the ball further than I go on my holidays."? **Lee Trevino**

62. Who hosted TV's chat show *Last Resort*? **Jonathan Ross**

63. Who said: "Much may be made of a Scotchman, if he be caught young."? **Dr Johnson**

64. What is the main feature of hypostyle in architecture? **Pillars (Supporting roof)**

65. What is MEZ? **Central European Time**

66. Who had Top Ten hits with *Searchin'*, *Whatever I Do* and *Who's Leaving Who*? **Hazell Dean**

67. In films, who played Bomba, the Jungle Boy? **Johnny Sheffield**

68. Was a pandour a soldier, a fiddle or a bed-curtain? **A soldier**

69. 'Horse opera' is a popular expression for what? **A Western film**

70. Who was the first human to make two space flights? **Gus Grissom**

71. Which British boxer beat Don Curry to become undisputed World Welterweight Champion in 1986? **Lloyd Honeyghan**

72. A sidereal day is the time taken for a star to go round what? **The Pole Star**

73. Who narrates the novel *A Kind of Loving*? **Vic Brown**

74. Is scaglia a type of moss, a pasta dish or a chalky limestone? **Chalky limestone**

75. Who, on a ship, is a nip-cheese? **The purser**

76. Which is the odd one out in this group: bichon frisé, Blue Bristol, Weimaraner or Kerry Blue? **Blue Bristol (It is a cat – the others are dogs)**

77. What did the Romans keep in an acetabulum? **Vinegar**

78. Which body of high-ranking laymen and ecclesiastics advised the Anglo-Saxon kings on major policy matters?
The Witan

79. Whose TV sketch of a cat in a microwave caused an uproar? **Hale and Pace's**

80. Which word means a butterfly, a handsome man and a flower? **Adonis**

81. Who played the title role in the 1949 film *Christopher Columbus*? **Fredric March**

82. What is the source of pumice stone? **Volcanoes**

83. In which game could you have an inwick? **Curling**

84. True or false: Ron Clarke broke 18 World records in athletics but never won an Olympic gold medal? **True**

85. Who had Top Ten hits with *The Magic Number* and *Ring Ring Ring*? **De La Soul**

86. Who wrote the novel *England Made Me*?
Graham Greene

87. Which opera contains *The Dance of the Comedians*?
The Bartered Bride

88. What would be kept in an etui? **Pins, needles, etc**

89. In which Dickens novel do Sir Leicester and Lady Honoria Dedlock appear? ***Bleak House***

90. Which motor-racing team was created by Colin Chapman?
Lotus

91. Who directed the film *8½*? **Federico Fellini**

92. If you are esurient, are you rich, hungry or lustful?
Hungry

93. In space, what did Hubble classify as elliptical, spiral and irregular? **Galaxies**

94. What name was given to those members of the audience who stood on the floor of the theatre in Shakepeare's time? **Groundlings**

95. Who hosted the TV series *Pass the Buck*? **George Layton**

96. Which was the first country to win the Football World Cup outside its own country? **Italy (1938)**

97. Of which country are the Coral Sea Islands a territory? **Australia**

98. People in Baltic regions often kept a zaltys as a symbol of wealth and fertility: what is a zaltys? **A snake**

99. Complete this Biblical quotation: "Ye blind guides, which strain at a gnat and . . ." **Swallow a camel**

100. For which American band leader did Stravinsky compose his *Ebony Concerto*? **Woody Herman**

Quiz 7 .

1. What do you do if you 'levant'? **Abscond, run away (usually leaving debts)**

2. Which famous singing group appeared in the film *Rock All Night*? **The Platters**

3. Which shrub is also known as the dwale? **Deadly nightshade or belladonna**

4. On TV who created the character Delbert Wilkins? **Lenny Henry**

5. What is the main vegetable in hummus? **Chick peas**

6. Which meteorological feature is measured in oktas: wind speed, cloud cover or permafrost? **Cloud cover**

7. Which creature produces the epicurean delicacy green fat? **The turtle**

8. Which country is the setting for the novel *The Good Earth*? **China**

9. Which Widnes player became the first Rugby League player to be transferred (to Wigan) for £100,000? **Joe Lydon**

10. Which spaghetti Western was a remake of the Japanese film *Yojimbo*? ***A Fistful of Dollars***

11. Who played the cab-driver in TV's *Streets Apart*? **James Hazeldine**

12. True or false: the rotula is another name for the elbow? **False (the knee-cap)**

13. Where is Mount Vinson the highest mountain? **Antarctica**

14. For what does AWACS stand? **Airborne Warning And Control System**

15. Who would wear a chador? **Muslim women**

16. Who owned a dog called Flush? **Elizabeth Barrett Browning**

17. Is a drumlin a percussion instrument, a species of duck or a hill? **A hill**

18. Which employee of an insurance company calculates probabilities? **An actuary**

19. In which athletics event did Britain's Wendy Norman become World Champion? **Modern Pentathlon**

20. How many horses pull a random? **Three**

21. In which country is Lake Volta? **Ghana**

22. Which organisation was founded in 1855 by Emma Robarts and Mary Jane Kinnaird? **YWCA**

23. Whose Top Ten hits included *Angel Face*, *Just For You* and *The Tears I Cried*? **The Glitter Band**

24. By what name was cartoonist Victor Weisz known? **Vicky**

25. Who played the old lady the crooks could not kill in the film *The Ladykillers*? **Katy Johnson**

26. What did Jethro Tull invent in 1701? **The seed drill**

27. Who was the girl who said "Oi'll give it foive" on TV's *Thank Your Lucky Stars*? **Janice Nicholls**

28. In a nursery rhyme, who wore a yellow petticoat and a green gown? **Daffy-down-Dilly**

29. What were the brick-built temple towers of ancient Mesopotamia called? **Ziggurats**

30. Who played the contract killer in the film *This Gun For Hire*? **Alan Ladd**

31. Which tennis player appeared in 8 consecutive US Open finals in the 1980s? **Ivan Lendl**

32. Hoba West, Cape York, Bacubirito and Armanty are all sites of what? **Where meteorites hit the earth**

33. For what were fossickers searching? **Gold or precious stones**

34. Whose Top Ten hits included *Live Forever*, *Cigarettes and Alcohol* and *Whatever*? **Oasis**

35. From what did Australian Aborigines make the drink beal? **Honey**

36. True or false: formerly corvée was a form of body armour?

    False (It was an obligation to perform a day's unpaid labour for a feudal lord)

37. What does a spheksophobist fear? **Wasps**

38. Who wrote the poem *An Irish Airman Foresees His Death*? **W B Yeats**

39. Which sense depends on the gustatory nerve? **Taste**

40. On 1960s TV who was Terry Brooks?

    The Milky Bar Kid

41. Which creatures are pavonine? **Peacocks**

42. Is purfling ornamental bordering, stealing or cooking in clay? **Ornamental bordering**

43. Which word can go before knife, catcher, bed and sauce?

    Oyster

44. Whom did Kevin Keegan succeed as Newcastle United manager in 1992? **Osvaldo Ardiles**

45. Is a stylops a marine creature, an insect or an architectural feature? **An insect**

46. If you bought the following items packaged and did not open them, which would keep the longest: plain biscuits, custard powder, plain flour or ground coffee?

    Ground coffee

47. Who played a German spy in the film *The Eye of the Needle*? **Donald Sutherland**

48. Who played Father Matthew in TV's *Father Matthew's Daughter*? **James Bolam**

49. Who said: "Ours [our army] is composed of the scum of the earth."? **Duke of Wellington**

50. Which famous novel was subtitled *Life Among the Lowly*?
Uncle Tom's Cabin

51. Which word means a strong taste, a projecting piece, a seaweed and a ringing noise? **Tang**

52. Who wrote the operas *Nelson, A Dinner Engagement* and *Castaway*? **Lennox Berkeley**

53. Joseph Bonaparte was installed as king of which country in 1808? **Spain**

54. In which city is the Rijksmuseum? **Amsterdam**

55. What is the common name for odontalgia? **Toothache**

56. What stopped play during the 1st India v Pakistan Test Match in 1979? **Swarm of bees**

57. Who had No 1 hits with *Clair* and *Get Down*?
Gilbert O'Sullivan

58. Is a picaroon a vagabond, a magpie or a high collar?
Vagabond

59. Where would you find cerumen?
In your ear (It is earwax)

60. What is the capital of British Columbia? **Victoria**

61. Whose comedy TV series was *Looking through the Cakehole*? **Jo Brand**

62. If you had bumbo would you play it, eat it or drink it?
Drink it (Punch)

63. Who played the title role in the 1947 film *The Bishop's Wife*? **Loretta Young**

64. Which word means to fill with holes, a puzzle and a coarse sieve? **Riddle**

65. In which English city, on the Ouse, would you find King's School and a cathedral with a central octagon? **Ely**

66. Which composer, son of a farmer, was taught music by Franck, became accompanist and servant to Porpora and spent 30 years as kappellmeister to the Esterhazy family?
Haydn

67. On which omnibus was the man meant to represent the ordinary man? **Clapham**

68. What do the British call what the Americans call a cootie?
A head louse

69. Who was the Princess Royal from 1932 to 1965?
Princess Mary

70. What colour is Pudsey Bear's eye bandage?
White with red spots

71. Under what name did musician Ellas McDaniel become famous? **Bo Diddley**

72. Who wrote *The Owl Service* and *The Stone Quartet*?
Alan Garner

73. Who presented *Police 5* on TV? **Shaw Taylor**

74. Who composed the operettas *The Firefly* and *The Vagabond King*? **Rudolf Friml**

75. Which council of 664 AD accepted Catholicism as the religion of Britain? **The Synod of Whitby**

76. About what do Malcolm Gluck and Oz Clarke write?
Wine

77. Who led the miners in the strike which led to the General Strike? **A J Cook**

78. True or false: William IV was the son of George III?
True

79. Is a cervelat a cat-like animal, a sausage or a muscle in the neck? **A sausage**

80. Which country owns the Caprivi Strip? **Namibia**

81. What kind of fruit is a rennet? **An apple**

82. What was the trade name for the blend of Merino wool and long staple cotton produced by the Hollins family from near Matlock? **Vyella**

83. Whose Top Ten hits included *She Makes My Day*, *Addicted To Love* and *I'll Be Your Baby Tonight*? **Robert Palmer**

84. Who made a solo flight from Britain to Australia in 1929-30 and won the first solo transatlantic yacht race in 1960? **Francis Chichester**

85. Which film made a star of Italian actress Silvana Mangano? ***Bitter Rice***

86. Name the title of the TV pop quiz hosted by Mark Lamarr with Sean Hughes and Phil Jupitus. ***Never Mind the Buzzcocks***

87. Which cricketer said: "Nobody's perfect. You know what happened to the last man who was – they crucified him."? **Geoffrey Boycott**

88. Which popular food dish was first mentioned in a report of 1876? **Fish and chips**

89. How did Australia prevent New Zealand from scoring the six they needed to win off the last ball of a match at Melbourne in 1981? **The ball was bowled underarm**

90. Which British monarch reportedly said: "I hate all boets and bainters"? **George I**

91. In mythology, what sprang from the blood of Medusa? **Pegasus**

92. What does an odometer measure? **Distance travelled**

93. Who won Best Actress Oscar for her performance in the film *Jezebel*? **Bette Davis**

94. What is made in a chessel? **Cheese**

95. Where in London is the Royal Horticultural Society's annual Flower Show held?
In the grounds of Chelsea Hospital

96. True or false: *The Happy Wanderer* was the only No 1 hit for the Obernkirchen Children's Choir?
False (It only reached No 2)

97. Which Leeds United player signed for Juventus for £70,000 in 1950? **John Charles**

98. Which Australian birds can be seen on the lake at Chartwell, Winston Churchill's former home?
Black swans

99. Who wrote *A Summer Bird-Cage* and *The Radiant Way*?
Margaret Drabble

100. Name the theme music of *The Archers*. *Barwick Green*

Quiz 8

1. In which medium was jeweller René Lalique an artist-craftsman? **Glass**

2. Which chocolate bar was advertised on TV as tasting as good as a '66 Mustang? **Maverick**

3. Which British swimmer won gold medals at the 1983, 1985, 1987 and 1989 European Championships, Commonwealth golds in 1982 and 1986 and Olympic gold in 1986? **Adrian Moorhouse**

4. What is the name of Postman Pat's wife? **Sara**

5. Who had Top Twenty hits with *It's a Man's Man's Man's World*, *Living In America* and *The Payback Mix*?
James Brown

6. Who played twins in the film *Dead Ringers*?
Jeremy Irons

7. And who played twins and his own father in the film *Raising Cain*? **John Lithgow**

8. Who wrote *The Remembered Kiss*, *The Man In Her Life* and *Steering By a Star*? **Ruby M Ayres**

9. In which TV series did Sarah Lancashire play a district nurse? ***Where the Heart Is***

10. Is a dziggetai a Babylonian temple, a wild ass or a tropical plant? **A wild ass**

11. Which word means a tract of upland, soft plumage and at a low level? **Down**

12. True or false: cirrostratus are classed as low clouds?
False (High)

13. Which word can mean to worry or tease, a painting brush and an angler's fly? **Badger**

14. Who were the first British football club to win two European trophies? **Tottenham Hotspur**

15. Who became leader of the Labour Party in 1980?
Michael Foot

16. In which TV series does Kyle Chandler play a stockbroker who knows the next day's news? ***Early Edition***

17. What sort of creature is a smew: a water rodent, a duck or a lizard? **A duck**

18. In which city is the Golden Hall of the Musikverein?
Vienna

19. Who wrote the book *Alias Mrs Doubtfire*?   **Anne Fine**

20. Is a stornello a type of cherry, a breed of sheep or a folk-song?   **Folk-song**

21. Who had Top Twenty hits with *I'm Not Scared* and *Cross My Heart*?   **Eighth Wonder**

22. Of which sport is savate a variety?
Boxing (uses feet as well as hands)

23. From which song do these words come: "And a hay harvest breeze / Blade on the feather / Shade off the trees"?   **Eton Boating Song**

24. What are Montrose, Beryl, Thelma, Magnus and Auk?
North Sea Oilfields

25. Was a dromond a clan leader, a standing stone or a ship?
A ship

26. Who was the first tennis-player to be defaulted from a Grand Slam Tournament (1990)?   **John McEnroe**

27. In which film did Gene Kelly dance with Jerry the cartoon mouse?   ***Anchors Aweigh***

28. Who wrote *The Viper of Milan*, *The Glen o' Weeping* and *I Will Maintain*?   **Marjorie Bowen**

29. Who painted *Burial of Count Orgaz*?   **El Greco**

30. Who became Commander-in-Chief of the UN Forces in Korea in 1950?   **General MacArthur**

31. What was the name of the model new town founded by Lord Leverhulme?   **Port Sunlight**

32. After the marriage of Louis VII of France was annulled in 1152 which other king did his ex-wife marry?
Henry II of England

33. Who sent this message in 1914: "My centre is giving way, my right is in retreat; situation excellent. I am attacking."?
Marshal Foch

34. Who played the evil Kurgan in the film *Highlander*?
Clancy Brown

35. What does the turbary give?
The right to dig turf or peat on another's land

36. Is a sephen a sting-ray, a sweetened drink or a poisonous fungus?
A sting-ray

37. Who presented the TV show *Whatever You Want*?
Gaby Roslin

38. Which footballer of the 1970s was nicknamed 'Supersub'?
David Fairclough

39. Is a Huon pine a species of yew, spruce or birch?   **Yew**

40. Which word can mean the devil, the morning-star and a match?
Lucifer

41. True or false: a sallet was a soldier's helmet?   **True**

42. What do we sing to the tune *America*?
God Save the Queen (King)

43. Who had Top Ten hits with *Stay With Me*, *Cindy Incidentally* and *Pool Hall Richard*?   **Faces**

44. If farmworkers were carrying out sartage what would they be doing?
Clearing woodland

45. Who was the first ever jump jockey to win 200 races in a season?
Peter Scudamore

46. Who created the Barry MacKenzie comic strip?
Barry Humphries

47. Who wandered around celebrities' homes in the TV series *Through the Keyhole*? **Loyd Grossman**

48. From what is the foodstuff tofu made?
Soya beans (curd)

49. Who played Vic Dakin in the film *Villain*?
Richard Burton

50. Of which country was the sovereign known as negus?
Ethiopia

51. Whose Top Twenty hits included *Call Me, Faithful* and *Tracks of My Tears*? **Go West**

52. For whose coronation was the *Crown Imperial March* composed? **George VI's**

53. Is a sambar a large deer, a silk tunic or a Japanese musical instrument? **A large deer**

54. Of what did Edward Heath say: "It is the unpleasant and unacceptable face of capitalism."? **The Lonrho Affair**

55. In which branch of the arts was Hamada Shoji world famous? **Pottery**

56. In which sport was Martine Le Moignan the first British woman to win a world title? **Squash**

57. Who was the mother of Mary I? **Catherine of Aragon**

58. Who played the lead in the original film of *The Nutty Professor*? **Jerry Lewis**

59. What was a tester or testril? **A coin**

60. Who commanded the winning side at the battle of Cannae? **Hannibal**

61. Name the resident cook on TV's *Food and Drink.*
Michael Barry

62. Which gulf lies between the Chinese island of Hainan and Vietnam? **Gulf of Tongkin**

63. In a famous story, who visited London, Paris and Vienna with Lorelei Lee? **Dorothy**

64. Where would you usually find sheers?
In dockyards (It is a lifting apparatus)

65. Who had Top Ten hits with *Me and You and a Dog Named Boo* and *I'd Love You To Want Me*? **Lobo**

66. Which planet was first named Georgium Sidus by Herschel? **Uranus**

67. Which entertainer's catchphrase was "God is love, but get it in writing."? **Gypsy Rose Lee's**

68. Which part of the body could be described as 'crinal'?
The hair

69. Which singing group were featured in the film *Can't Stop the Music*? **The Village People**

70. Is Shelta a type of porcelain, a rock found near beaches or a secret language?
Secret language (used by tinkers and beggars)

71. Where would you have found a serdab?
In an Egyptian tomb

72. Under what name did Lazlo Loewenstein achieve fame in films? **Peter Lorre**

73. Who presented the TV series *In Suspicious Circumstances*? **Edward Woodward**

74. If you had tzimmes (or tsimmes) would you see a doctor, eat it or feed them? **Eat it (It is a stew)**

75. Which Liberal politician was MP for Orkney and Shetland from 1950 to 1983? **Jo Grimond**

76. Which organisation has its HQ at Langley, Virginia, in the USA? **CIA**

77. Which famous US General was accidentally shot and killed by his own men in May 1863?
Gen T J 'Stonewall' Jackson

78. Whose first Top Ten hit was *See Emily Play*?
Pink Floyd

79. What would you be making if you used a pontil?
Glass (Iron rod)

80. Who played the title role in the film *Annie Oakley*?
Barbara Stanwyck

81. Which city in Africa is also called Kaapstad?
Cape Town

82. Is a saw-whet a stone for sharpening saws, a plant yielding a yellow dye or a small owl? **A small owl**

83. In which sport was Mick Cronin a famous international player? **Rugby Union Football**

84. What was the famous advice given by *Punch* magazine to those about to marry? **Don't!**

85. True or false: a Chinese novelist used the pen name Ding Ling? **True**

86. Which surname is common to a Scottish heroine, a British PM and a TV newsreader? **MacDonald**

87. What was the surname of Little Nell in *The Old Curiosity Shop*? **Trent**

88. How many Brandenburg Concertos are there: 4, 5 or 6?
6

89. Which Scottish regiment is called The Black Watch?
42nd Highland Regiment

90. Who had a Top Ten hit with *Snoopy Vs The Red Baron*?
Royal Guardsmen

91. Name the real person behind Rab C Nesbitt on TV.
Gregor Fisher

92. What was the name of the detective played by Frank Sinatra in the film *Lady In Cement*? **Tony Rome**

93. A criosphinx had the head of which creature? **A sheep**

94. As what did Rosella Hightower achieve fame?
A ballerina/dancer

95. Which famous G B Shaw play has characters called Lavinia, Spinthio and Ferravius?
Androcles and the Lion

96. Under what name is Margaretha Geertruida Zelle remembered in history? **Mata Hari**

97. Name the TV village patrolled by Hamish MacBeth.
Lochdubh

98. Which British Football club signed the Brazilian Juninho in 1995? **Middlesbrough**

99. In which Carry On film did Kenneth Williams exit with the words "Frying tonight!"? ***Carry On Screaming***

100. Which Royal House ruled Scotland before the House of Stuart? **The House of Bruce**

Quiz 9

1. Under what name did René Raymond write gangster stories? **James Hadley Chase**

2. Who had No 1 hits with *Bohemian Rhapsody* and *Innuendo*? **Queen**

3. Where would you see a seiche?

On Swiss lakes (It is a wave)

4. Name one of the two countries through which the Western Bug River runs? **Ukraine or Poland**

5. Which bird is sometimes called the spink?

The finch (chaffinch)

6. In which film did Jodie Foster sing *My Name Is Tallulah*?

Bugsy Malone

7. What relation was Charles II to James II? **Brother**

8. Name the TV series starring James McPherson as Michael Jardine. ***Taggart***

9. Which royal post has been held by William Cusins, Walter Parratt, Walford Davies and Arnold Bax?

Master of the King's (Queen's) Music

10. Who was the first cricketer to take 250 Test wickets?

Fred Trueman

11. Which collection of plays was published by actors John Heminge and Henry Condell?

(Shakespeare's) *First Folio*

12. What title is given to the senior prelate in the Roman Catholic church in England and Wales?

Archbishop of Westminster

13. True or false: David Owen was MP for Portsmouth Southsea? **False (Plymouth Devonport)**

14. Which annual race takes place on the Boat Race course in reverse? **Head of the River Race**

15. Who had a 1994 No 1 hit with *Inside*? **Stiltskin**

16. What are Old Boys of Charterhouse School called?

Old Carthusians

17. Which US film had the British title *Meet Whiplash Willie*?
The Fortune Cookie

18. Which novelist also used the names Sheila Barnes, Mary Essex and Rachel Harvey? **Ursula Bloom**

19. Name the actress playing Stella in the TV series *Is It Legal*. **Imelda Staunton**

20. What was the Shirelles' only Top Ten hit?
Will You Still Love Me Tomorrow?

21. Is a vettura a four-wheeled carriage, a soft hat or flowering shrub? **A four-wheeled carriage**

22. Who said in 1963: "England will win the World Cup in 1966."? **Alf Ramsey**

23. Who expounded the system of church government known as Presbyterianism? **John Calvin**

24. Of which country was Cambyses the ruler? **Persia**

25. In which English city would you see the Eastgate Clock, the Grosvenor Museum and the Roodee? **Chester**

26. With which industry is Wardour Street in London associated? **The film industry**

27. In 1976, which newspaper became Britain's largest-selling daily paper? **The *Sun***

28. Is the principal vein of a leaf a ribbin, a nervure or a ventril? **A nervure**

29. Who wrote *Smith*, *Black Jack* and *The Apprentices*?
Leon Garfield

30. Which New Zealand rugby player was nicknamed 'The Boot'? **Don Clarke**

31. Which Cornish town has an annual Furry dance?
Helston

32. Of whom is the famous Droeshout Portrait?
William Shakespeare

33. Who wrote the poem that begins: "There's a breathless hush in the close tonight. Ten to make and the match to win."?
Henry Newbolt

34. Who played Jack the Ripper's murderous daughter in the film *Hands of the Ripper*?
Angharad Rees

35. Which college did Rik Mayall and his friends represent on *University Challenge* in an episode of *The Young Ones*?
Scumbag College

36. Whose house, Hill Top, is kept as a museum today?
Beatrix Potter's

37. Which word means a short-handled shovel, a device to spoon out ice-cream and an exclusive piece of news?
Scoop

38. Is an orarion a prayer-mat, a deacon's stole or a lectern?
A deacon's stole

39. Who had Top Ten hits with *Indiana Wants Me* and *There's a Ghost in the House*?
R Dean Taylor

40. Which West Indian bowler took 135 wickets during the 1950 tour of England?
Sonny Ramahdin

41. Who wrote *Billy Liar* and *Jeffrey Bernard Is Unwell*?
Keith Waterhouse

42. True or false: Rodgers and Hart wrote *My Fair Lady*?
False (Lerner and Loewe did)

43. Which sport featured in the film *Kansas City Bomber*?
Roller-skating

44. Name the actor connecting *Rhodes*, *Drop the Dead Donkey* and *Between the Lines* on TV.
Neil Pearson

45. What was a bridewell?
Prison, house of correction

46. By what collective name were the seven Anglo-Saxon kingdoms known? **Heptarchy**

47. Who would use a sordine in his job: a painter, a musician or a sailor? **A musician (It is a mute for an instrument)**

48. Which popular radio series had characters called Coatsleeve Charlie, Lord Dockyard and Grizelda Pugh? ***Hancock's Half Hour***

49. Which element takes its name from the Greek for 'stench'? **Bromine**

50. In the International Code of Flag Signals what does G mean? **I require a pilot**

51. What are branle, chaconne, gigue and morisca? **Dances**

52. If you are costive, are you angry, extremely placid or constipated? **Constipated**

53. True or false: a costmary was a lady-in-waiting? **False (It is an aromatic plant)**

54. Who was the lady who vanished in the film *The Lady Vanishes*? **Miss Froy**

55. Which English batsman scored 905 runs in five Test matches in Australia in 1929? **Wally Hammond**

56. Architecturally, where would you find an abacus? **At the top of a column**

57. Where would you find a fire-dog? **In a fireplace!**

58. Which comedienne had a TV series called *Murder Most Horrid*? **Dawn French**

59. Which was the main British fighter plane used in the Battle of Britain? **Hurricane**

60. What name is given to the spring term at Oxford and Dublin universities? **Hilary**

61. What connects Chalgrove Field, Stratton, Lansdowne and Winceby?   **They were battles in the English Civil War**

62. Which wanted man helped David Balfour in the novel *Kidnapped*?   **Alan Breck**

63. Is a hanap a type of rough woollen sack, a basket or a goblet?   **A goblet**

64. What does the abbreviation AONB stand for?   **Area of Outstanding Natural Beauty**

65. Which tennis player lost in the Wimbledon Men's Singles Final in 1954, 1956, 1970 and 1974?   **Ken Rosewall**

66. With whom did William Holden fall in love in the film *Love Is a Many Splendoured Thing*?   **Jennifer Jones**

67. Who composed *A Village Romeo and Juliet*, *In a Summer Garden* and *Brigg Fair*?   **Delius**

68. In which US city is Hartsfield International Airport?   **Atlanta**

69. Which religion has the Five Ks as shared symbols?   **Sikhism**

70. Which children's character was created by John Cunliffe and Ivor Wood?   **Postman Pat**

71. Which British battleship was rammed by the *Camperdown* of its own fleet and sank with heavy loss of life in June, 1893?   **HMS *Victoria***

72. Who replaced Bamber Gascoigne as questionmaster on TV's *University Challenge*?   **Jeremy Paxman**

73. In which sport was Richard Bergmann World Champion several times?   **Table tennis**

74. Is frazil a type of embroidery, anchor-ice or a joint in woodworking?   **Anchor-ice**

75. From which language does the word 'bungalow' come?
Bengali [Accept Hindi.]

76. Who invented the pneumatic tyre? **John Dunlop**

77. Which radio series had the signature tune *The Devil's Galop*? ***Dick Barton – Special Agent***

78. What was the real name of British bandleader Geraldo?
Gerald Bright

79. Who wrote the play *A Voyage Round My Father*?
John Mortimer

80. On which island is Port-au-Prince? **Hispaniola**

81. Which word means a tree, a sea inlet, to bark hoarsely and a compartment in a ship? **Bay**

82. In which country is the book and film *The Moon Is Down* set? **Norway**

83. Who was James Durie, in an R L Stevenson novel?
The Master of Ballantrae

84. True or false: G B Shaw lived for almost fifty years in Ayot St Lawrence? **True**

85. What is a judge called in Scotland? **A sheriff**

86. Name the topic of the TV programme *The White Room*.
Music

87. What is a maar? **A type of volcanic crater**

88. With which sport would you associate Jeannette Altwegg?
Ice-skating

89. Who would play the melody a ranz-des-vaches?
A cattle herdsman

90. Who wrote *Our Town*, *The Skin of Our Teeth* and *The Bridge of San Luis Rey*? **Thornton Wilder**

91. What kind of weaves are velvet, corduroy, plush and velour? **Pile weaves**

92. What was the nationality of the last non-Italian Pope before Pope John Paul II? **Dutch**

93. If you ganched, would you sell curios, fish with several hooks on a line or impale someone? **Impale someone**

94. Which is the oldest regiment in Britain? **The Honourable Artillery Company**

95. On TV whom did Julia Jekyll turn into? **Harriet Hyde**

96. Which maidens in Norse mythology rule the fates of men? **The Norns**

97. Who played Professor Quatermass in the films *The Quatermass Experiment* and *Quatermass II*? **Brian Donlevy**

98. Who was the first US President to watch a cricket Test Match? **Dwight D Eisenhower**

99. What kind of triangle has no sides equal? **A scalene triangle**

100. Which radio service is based at Bush House? **BBC's World Service**

Quiz 10

1. In which film did Elvis Presley play Vince Everett? *Jailhouse Rock*

2. Who were the first people to operate commando units? **The Boers**

3. For whom was the Moon alphabet devised? **The blind**

4. Is a chibouk a wind, a long pipe for smoking or a tropical flea? **A long pipe**

5. Which element has the chemical symbol Fr? **Francium**

6. Who is the patron saint of electricians? **St Lucy**

7. What is the final stage in the passage of a bill before it becomes an Act of Parliament? **The Royal Assent**

8. The story *Elinor and Marianne* was re-written and published in 1811 under what new title?
Sense and Sensibility

9. Name the TV series featuring characters called Tina Dingle, Linda Glover and Sophie Wright. **Emmerdale**

10. Whom did West Ham United beat to win the European Cup Winners Cup in 1965? **Munich 1860**

11. Who played the male lead in the film *The Snows of Kilimanjaro*? **Gregory Peck**

12. Which famous hotel was the first important steel-framed building in London? **The Ritz**

13. Who was *The Tenant of Wildfell Hall*? **Helen Graham**

14. What would hang on a rannel-tree? **Cooking utensils**

15. Is a springe a rock plant, a snare or a small stream?
A snare

16. Which word means a measure equal to one quarter of a chain, a rest for birds or a freshwater fish? **Perch**

17. What is the capital of Papua New Guinea?
Port Moresby

18. True or false: the first British census was held in 1821?
False (1801)

19. Which novel has characters called Herbert Pocket, Bently Drummle and Joe Gargery? **Great Expectations**

20. Which animal is also known as the seecawk? **The skunk**

21. What powered Stefan Ptacek's aircraft on a cross-Channel flight in 1981? **Solar cells**

22. Which composer wrote the most concertos? **Vivaldi**

23. What was the name of the character played by Danny John Jules in the TV comedy *Red Dwarf*? **Cat**

24. On what would bandoline be used? **The hair (To keep it flat)**

25. Who played the hunted CIA researcher in the film *Three Days of the Condor*? **Robert Redford**

26. Which then male-only event did Roberta Gibb and Kathy Switzer take part in in 1967? **The Boston Marathon**

27. Which precious object was found at Athelney in Somerset in 1693? **The Alfred Jewel**

28. In which country was the Carnatic War fought? **India**

29. Which conspiracy was led by Arthur Thistlewood? **Cato Street Conspiracy**

30. What was the name of Miss Marple's nephew? **Raymond**

31. Who won a Grammy Award for his recording of *Tears in Heaven* in 1992? **Eric Clapton**

32. Who replaced Will Carling as England Rugby Union captain in 1996? **Phil de Glanville**

33. Which word means a covering on a cannon, a stage extension and a protective garment? **Apron**

34. True or false: a rosery is a place where roses grow? **True**

35. Who played Hyacinth's brother-in-law in TV's *Keeping Up Appearances*? **Geoffrey Hughes**

36. Who did Natalie Wood's singing in the film *West Side Story*? **Marni Nixon**

37. Who wrote the poems *The Dunciad* and *Epistle To Arbuthnot*? **Alexander Pope**

38. Whose Top Ten hits included *It's All In The Game*, *I'm The Lonely One* and *Constantly*? **Cliff Richard**

39. If an item on a menu has 'veronique' after it, with what will it be served? **White grapes**

40. Who played Elizabeth I in the 1971 film *Mary, Queen of Scots*? **Glenda Jackson**

41. When the football club Moscow Dynamo toured Britain in 1945, where did they insist they eat their meals? **At the Russian Embassy**

42. Is a tourbillion an African bird, a firework or a worsted material? **A firework**

43. In which TV series did removal men Alf and Bert encourage literacy? *On the Move*

44. True or false: Dennis Price murdered eight people in the film *Kind Hearts and Coronets*? **False (Some of them died natural or accidental deaths)**

45. Which word means a piece of cloth, a mark for archers to shoot at and a blow with the hand? **Clout**

46. Who wrote *The Scarlet Letter*, *The Marble Faun* and *The Blithedale Romance*? **Nathaniel Hawthorne**

47. In which TV series did John Cater play a hall porter with a dog called Jumbo? *The Duchess of Duke Street*

48. What was unusual about Scott Welland's run of 4 hours 7 minutes 54 seconds in the Detroit Marathon of 1982? **He ran backwards**

49. Which Italian composer, who wrote 115 operas, was Queen Christina of Sweden's private conductor at her private theatre in Rome? **Antonio Scarlatti**

50. Which king's reign is the subject of the Second Book of Samuel in the Bible? **David's**

51. What is glossolalia?
Speaking in unknown or foreign tongues (in trances, etc)

52. In which country are the cities of Plovdiv, Varna and Burgas? **Bulgaria**

53. True or false: Queen Victoria had a sister? **False**

54. Which film character got *Spring Fever*, was laughed at and found *Love*, had a *Double Life* and *Blonde Trouble*?
Andy Hardy

55. Is griseofulvin an antibiotic, a grey silken textile or a style of painting on glass? **An antibiotic**

56. Who had Top Ten hits with *Kisses Sweeter Than Wine*, *Kewpie Doll* and *There Must Be a Way*?
Frankie Vaughan

57. In which World Championship in 1936 did the playing of the first point between Alex Erlich and Fareas Paneth last for more than two hours? **Table tennis**

58. Which character did Peter Davison play in the TV series *All Creatures Great and Small*? **Tristram Farnon**

59. What name is given to a number that cannot be expressed as a fraction or ratio? **An irrational number**

60. Which Scottish chemist discovered the noble gases?
Sir William Ramsay

61. What name is given to a situation where the supply of a product is controlled by a few large producers?
An oligopoly

62. In Oriental mythology what was the fung or fum?

A fabulous bird

63. Andorra has as joint heads of state Spain's Bishop of Urgel and . . . who? **The President of France**

64. Which non-league football team famously trained on a diet of glucose, eggs and sherry and knocked First Division Sunderland out of the FA Cup in 1949?

Yeovil Town

65. In which film did commuter Michael Douglas crack and take revenge on the system? *Falling Down*

66. Who composed *Der Rosenkavalier*? **Richard Strauss**

67. What does the abbreviation DSN stand for?

Deep Space Network

68. In Morse Code which number is represented by five dots?

5!

69. When was the Berlin Wall built? **1961**

70. Of which republic did former Russian minister Edvard Shevardnadze become President? **Georgia**

71. Who had a 1975 No 1 hit with *January*? **Pilot**

72. Who was known as 'The Queen of Mean'?

Leona Helmsley

73. What would the British call what the Americans call a dry-goods store? **A draper's shop**

74. Who won the Battle of Lützen in 1632? **Sweden**

75. Who played Ernest Bishop in TV's *Coronation Street*?

Stephen Hancock

76. Who grants an indult? **The Pope**

77. What name is given to a part of a circle cut off by a line that is not a radius? **A segment**

78. Who wrote *The Golden Notebook* and *The Good Terrorist*? **Doris Lessing**

79. Which British band-leader (and later disc-jockey) had the signature tune *Make Those People Sway*? **Jack Jackson**

80. With which art movement is Georges Braque associated? **Cubism**

81. What name is given to the main vein and artery in the leg? **Femoral**

82. Which was the first club to win the FA Cup with only ten men? **Nottingham Forest**

83. What was the setting for the wartime mystery film *Green For Danger*? **A hospital**

84. Who played Saucy Nancy in the TV series *Worzel Gummidge*? **Barbara Windsor**

85. Where was the Group of Three set up in 1995? **South America**

86. Is a sarangi a monkey, a musical instrument or a tropical fish? **A musical instrument**

87. How many sides has a hendecagon? **11**

88. True or false: Mauritius is an independent republic? **True**

89. Who had Top Ten hits with *A Little Bit Me A Little Bit You* and *Alternate Title*? **The Monkees**

90. What was the nickname of Henry Armstrong, the first boxer to hold three World Titles simultaneously? **Homicide Hank**

91. In which city is Kingsford International Airport? **Sydney**

92. After whom are the Tony theatre awards named?
Antoinette Perry

93. Who was the first Pope? **St Peter**

94. Who wrote *The Dram Shop*, *Nana* and *La Débàcle*?
Émile Zola

95. In ancient Greece what was a stater? **A coin**

96. Who had Top Ten hits with *Girls*, *Dolly My Love* and
Jack In the Box? **Moments**

97. Who played the head of the family in the film *How Green
Was My Valley*? **Donald Crisp**

98. In which TV series was about-to-retire John Mills married
to Megs Jenkins? ***Young At Heart***

99. What does the musical direction *tenero* mean?
Tender, tenderly

100. Which country left the Commonwealth in 1949?
Republic of Ireland

Quiz 11

1. What sort of plants are the genus *Vanda*? **Orchids**

2. Of which country did Birendra become king in 1972?
Nepal

3. On which garment would you find a fourchette?
Gloves (The piece between fingers)

4. Which word means a radio-controlled plane, a deep
humming sound and a male bee? **Drone**

5. Which football club did Denis Law join for £100,000 in
1961? **Torino**

6. Barbara Gray was the central character of which TV drama series? **_Nanny_**

7. The Ferrara family were famous for the manufacture of what? **Swords**

8. What part was played by Henry Travers in the film _It's a Wonderful Life_? **An angel**

9. How many metres are there in a hectometre? **100**

10. Which is the largest religious denomination in Switzerland? **Roman Catholicism**

11. Who won the Booker Prize with _Moon Tiger_? **Penelope Lively**

12. Who was deposed in 1971 by General Idi Amin? **Milton Obote**

13. True or false: in 1945 the British electorate was more than 35 million? **False (33+)**

14. Which form of punishment consisted of drawing up an offender by a rope and letting him fall to the end of the rope? **Strappado**

15. In whose honour is the Festival of Hoolee? **Krishna**

16. Who was the first British female singer to have a No 1 hit (1953)? **Lita Roza**

17. What name is given to the 'musical' instrument consisting of a metal tube with a membrane covering a hole, through which one sings or hums? **A kazoo**

18. To which bird family does the chough belong? **Crow**

19. In which BAFTA-winning TV drama did Norman Wisdom play a man dying of cancer? **_Going Gently_**

20. Who directed the film _Picnic At Hanging Rock_? **Peter Weir**

21. Where did Swabians come from? **Germany**

22. Which country refused to play South Africa in the final of the 1974 Davis Cup? **India**

23. Is dartre a skin disease, an embroidery stitch or a kind of grass? **A skin disease**

24. What is tattersall? **A checked material**

25. Which word describes metal that can be drawn out into wire? **Ductile**

26. Who had a 1989 No 1 hit with *You'll Never Stop Me Loving You*? **Sonia**

27. Which poet wrote *Blind Fireworks* and *Autumn Journal*? **Louis Macneice**

28. Where would you wear a larrigan? **On your foot or leg (It is a high boot)**

29. Which football club won promotion to Division 1 in 1990, but were relegated to Division 3 immediately afterwards before being reinstated in Division 2 after an appeal? **Swindon**

30. Who played Edgar Pascoe in the TV drama series *The Fragile Heart*? **Nigel Hawthorne**

31. What are fastened to a swingle-tree? **A horse's traces**

32. Who was the first European to win the Indianapolis 500 after World War II? **Jim Clark**

33. What was the second film in which James Mason played Rommel? **The Desert Rats**

34. Which surname is shared by a British author, three US film actress sisters and a Canadian Prime Minister? **Bennett**

35. Of which country was Shakespeare's Cymbeline king?
Britain

36. Which is the second highest mountain in Africa?
Mount Kenya

37. Under what name did Nedra Talley, Veronica and Estelle Bennett record? **The Ronettes**

38. Which sport was played by 'The Gas House Gang'?
Baseball (St Louis Cardinals)

39. Which British ship was fired on and detained in the Yangtze River by the Chinese Communists in 1949?
HMS *Amethyst*

40. Which organisation entertained British forces during World War II? **ENSA**

41. Where in the British Isles would you find sheadings?
Isle of Man

42. Of what is semiotics the study?
Signs and symbols (and their relationships in language)

43. Which birds fly in a skein? **Geese or swans**

44. Is skat a whip, a card-game or a type of basketwork?
A card-game

45. True or false: Jaroslav Drobny's only Wimbledon Singles final was in 1954?
False (He was the beaten finalist in 1949 as well as 1954 winner)

46. What is the other title of Karl Denver's hit record *Wimoweh*? ***The Lion Sleeps Tonight***

47. Feodor Chaliapin was the first Russian to gain international stature as what? **Opera singer**

48. Which Muslim people were led in a guerilla war by Mustafa Barzani? **The Kurds**

49. Which character on TV was Lorraine's ex-husband, Bianca's father and Simon's brother? **David Wicks**

50. Where would a nesiote person live? **On an island**

51. Who played George Gershwin in the film *Rhapsody In Blue*? **Robert Alda**

52. In architecture, under what name did Charles Edouard Jeanneret-Gris become famous? **Le Corbusier**

53. For which product was the firm founded by J W Britain famous? **Model and toy soldiers**

54. What is the spiked wheel on a spur called? **Rowel**

55. Which word means a straw mattress, a wooden structure on which crates are stacked and a potter's tool? **Pallet**

56. Which novel, banned by the Nazis for its pacifism, had a sequel called *The Road Back*?
All Quiet On The Western Front

57. Which co-founder of the Black Consciousness Movement died in police custody in 1973? **Steve Biko**

58. Which monarch's illness occasioned the writing of *O God, Our Help In Ages Past*? **Queen Anne's**

59. Is a scutiger a centipede, a small shield or a soldier forced to serve by his master? **Centipede**

60. Who played Tremayne in the TV series *The Champions*?
Anthony Nicholls

61. Who was the film star brother of film star George Sanders? **Tom Conway**

62. In which country are the Zagros Mountains? **Iran**

63. What was the former name of Zaire? **Belgian Congo**

64. Who was Britain's first Olympic ski-jumper?

Eddie Edwards

65. Frank Foster took over the leadership of which famous orchestra when its leader died? **Count Basie Orchestra**

66. Who hosted the TV show *Cross Wits*? **Tom O'Connor**

67. Which Astaire/Rogers film contained the songs *Let's Face the Music and Dance*, *Let Yourself Go* and *We Saw the Sea*? **Follow the Fleet**

68. Of whom did Courtney Jones say: "They have opened up a new era, if only the rest of the world can grasp what they do."? **Torvill and Dean**

69. Whom did George Bush defeat in the 1988 US Presidential Election? **Michael Dukakis**

70. Which international organisation was founded in 1961 by Peter Benenson? **Amnesty International**

71. Who, in 1955, became England's youngest football international? **Duncan Edwards**

72. In what year did Edward Heath become leader of the Conservative party? **1965**

73. In which US state is Fort Lauderdale? **Florida**

74. Which song in 1979 was Cliff Richard's first No 1 hit since *Congratulations* in 1968?

We Don't Talk Anymore

75. True or false: Oksana Bayul was a world champion gymnast? **False (He was an ice-skater)**

76. What nationality are the audio and video manufacturers Bang and Olufsen? **Danish**

77. Which comedienne interviewed Sarah Ferguson at her home in 1996? **Ruby Wax**

78. What does the prefix "xero-" mean? **Dry**

79. What was the surname of the literary children John, Susan, Titty and Roger?
Walker (*Swallows and Amazons*)

80. Is a plafond a dais, a ceiling or a basement? **A ceiling**

81. Who was Derek in Derek and the Dominoes?
Eric Clapton

82. Of what is orismology the study?
Definitions and explanations

83. Who became the national football coach of Australia in 1996? **Terry Venables**

84. Which instrument did jazz musician John Coltrane play?
Saxophone

85. What was the nickname of gangster Charles Arthur Floyd?
Pretty Boy

86. On TV which family lived at 704 Houser Street in New York? **The Bunker family (*All in the Family*)**

87. On which animals is Jane Goodall a world authority?
Chimpanzees

88. What was The Pilgrimage of Grace?
An uprising (in Yorkshire in 1536)

89. Who played Mr Brown, Sykes' neighbour in TV's *Sykes*?
Richard Wattis

90. What is matelote? **A fish dish**

91. In the film *It's a Mad Mad Mad Mad World* who played Milton Berle's obnoxious mother-in-law? **Ethel Merman**

92. Who was the leader of the pop group Kilburn and the High Roads? **Ian Dury**

93. Whom did Mike Tyson beat in 1986 to become the youngest ever World Heavyweight Boxing Champion?
Trevor Berbick

94. When does an eye-servant work? **When watched!**

95. What is measured in phons? **Loudness**

96. Which supertanker sank off the Brittany coast in March 1978? *Amoco Cadiz*

97. Which model of car did Henry Ford name after his son?
The Edsel

98. In which TV series did Edward Woodward and Tim Healy play dustmen? *Common As Muck*

99. Which US soul singer was shot and killed by his father in a domestic dispute? **Marvin Gaye**

100. What do pulmonate creatures have? **Lungs**

Quiz 12

1. Who hosted the TV game *Win, Lose or Draw*?
Bob Mills

2. What is the common name for sycosis?
Barber's itch/rash

3. Which structures were attacked in the Rebecca Riots from 1839 to 1844? **Tollgates**

4. From where do Vandemonians come? **Tasmania**

5. Which nuts are used in the pastry frangipane or frangipani? **Almonds**

6. Who directed the films *California Split*, *Thieves Like Us* and *Brewster McCloud*? **Robert Altman**

7. Which TV programme, which began in 1971, has changed its name every year? **Film '71**

8. Which classic Cole Porter song is also known as *Volver A Empezar*? **Begin the Beguine**

9. Which motor company launched a car called The Ka? **Ford**

10. In which Shakespeare play are Phrygia and Timandry the mistresses of Alcibiades? **Timon of Athens**

11. Who wrote the jazz standards *Maiden Voyage*, *Dolphin Dance* and *Speak Like a Child*? **Herbie Hancock**

12. On which radio station would you have heard The Ovaltineys? **Radio Luxembourg**

13. Which national leader did Irishwoman Violet Gibson shoot and wound in 1926? **Benito Mussolini**

14. With what was the group Der Blaue Reiter concerned? **Painting**

15. In which country is Malin Head? **Republic of Ireland**

16. Who made Charlie McArthy and Mortimer Snerd famous? **Edgar Bergen**

17. In which small TV town did Mrs Corbett sell flowers in the market square? **Trumpton**

18. Who played the title role in Ken Russell's film *Mahler*? **Robert Powell**

19. Liz Mitchell, Marcia Barrett, Maize Williams and Bobby Farrell were which pop group? **Boney M**

20. Who would use tiver in their work: shepherds, potters or plasterers? **Shepherds (It's a dye)**

21. From which country does Tokay wine come? **Hungary**

22. Which maidens were sent by Odin to conduct the souls of slain warriors to Valhalla? **Valkyries**

23. Who co-presented TV's *Ready, Steady, Go!* and hosted the radio programme *Beat the Record*? **Keith Fordyce**

24. Who had a 1989 No 1 hit with *Ride On Time*? **Black Box**

25. In the film, who played *The Incredible Shrinking Man*? **Grant Williams**

26. Who wrote the book *The Life and Death of Mr Badman* which has characters called Mr Badman, Mr Attentive and Mr Wiseman? **John Bunyan**

27. Who played the Prince of Wales in the film *The Madness of King George*? **Rupert Everett**

28. What were first held in 776 BC? **Olympic Games**

29. In 1970, when South Africa cancelled its cricket tour of England, who played an unofficial Test series against England? **The Rest of the World**

30. Who composed *Carmina Burana*, *Prometheus* and *Die Kluge*? **Carl Orff**

31. Who played the title character in the radio drama series *Wallis – the Life and Loves of Wallis Simpson*? **Stockard Channing**

32. On children's TV, what sort of animal was Romuald? **A reindeer**

33. Which word means an immoral man, to slope backwards and a long-handled implement? **Rake**

34. In P G Wodehouse's stories what did Gussie Fink-Nottle study? **Newts**

35. Name the part of an animal called the lights. **The lungs**

36. Who had Top Ten hits with *Going Back, All I See Is You*, and *Losing You*? **Dusty Springfield**

37. If ursine is bearlike, what is suilline? **Pig-like**

38. Which sea-creature is sometimes called fire-flair? **Sting-ray**

39. In which country is the Pilbara Range? **Australia**

40. Which instrument did Joe 'King' Oliver play? **Cornet**

41. Which drink is also called wormwood? **Absinthe**

42. Which TV family's Christian names are Homer, Marge, Bart, Lisa and Maggie? ***The Simpsons***

43. True or false: Bunny Austin was the first man to wear shorts on the Wimbledon Centre Court in 1933? **True**

44. Which TV character of the 1970s and 1980s was called "Swine of the Decade"? **J R Ewing**

45. Who played Millicent Fritton, Headmistress of St Trinians in the film *The Belles of St Trinians*? **Alastair Sim**

46. Who wrote the plays *The Hairy Ape*, *The Great God Brown* and *Lazarus Laughed*? **Eugene O'Neill**

47. What was pop and country singer Ricky Nelson's Christian name? **Eric**

48. What word is used to distinguish a whole number from a fraction? **Integer**

49. Is a kipe a basket to catch fish in, a woman's petticoat or the skin of a calf? **Basket**

50. Who played Wally in both *Crocodile Dundee* films? **John Meillon**

51. Which high army rank was introduced in 1736? **Field Marshal**

52. In which wars were the Battles of Lang's Neck, Graspan, Stormberg and Lindley? **The Boer Wars**

53. Of which African country is Niamey the capital? **Niger**

54. Which shipping line owned the *Titanic*?
White Star Shipping Line

55. Is a coccagee a domestic fowl, a rosette or a kind of cider apple? **Kind of cider apple**

56. What is measured in coombs? **Corn**

57. Which treaty of 878 AD was made between Alfred and the Danes? **Treaty of Wedmore**

58. In which film was John Wayne killed by a giant squid?
Reap the Wild Wind

59. Who replaced Pete Duel in TV's *Alias Smith and Jones*?
Roger Davis

60. What moved to Nine Elms in 1974?
Covent Garden Fruit and Vegetable Market

61. Which golfer said: "I can't wait to get up in the morning to hear what I have to say."? **Lee Trevino**

62. Who had Top Ten hits with *Everybody Dance*, *Le Freak* and *Good Times*? **Chic**

63. Who played the Lord of Summerisle in the film *The Wicker Man*? **Christopher Lee**

64. To what use is the tin-foil tain put? **Backing mirrors**

65. The city of Fushun in China stands on one of the largest what in the world? **Coalfields**

66. Which group released albums called *Days of Future Passed*, *In Search of the Lost Chord* and *On the Threshold of a Dream*? **The Moody Blues**

67. What were first used in horse-racing at Newmarket in 1965? **Starting stalls**

68. True or false: Eliot Ness and the Untouchables were real law enforcers? **True**

69. Which island is separated from New Zealand by the Foveaux Strait? **Stewart Island**

70. What does a modiste make? **Hats and dresses**

71. Who confirmed the existence of radio waves? **Heinrich Hertz**

72. Who played Raquel in TV's *Only Fools and Horses*? **Tessa Peake-Jones**

73. Which stretch of water separates Madagascar from mainland Africa? **Mozambique Channel**

74. Who was on the British throne when British troops captured Washington and burnt the White House? **George III**

75. Which famous Institute of Art was established in London in 1929? **Courtauld Institute**

76. Who starred in the films *Call Me Madam*, *Singin' In The Rain* and *I Love Melvin*? **Donald O'Connor**

77. Which famous doctor made his debut in the story *Beyond This Place*? **Dr Finlay**

78. Which famous liner caught fire and capsized in New York in 1942? **The *Normandie***

79. What is venery? **Hunting, the chase**

80. Is a pressiroster someone who is interested in the past, an ancient coin or a wading bird? **A wading bird**

81. What was the name of John Cleland's *Woman of Pleasure*? **Fanny Hill**

82. What was once measured in lamberts?
Luminous brightness of a surface

83. Which word means a target, a parachute used to reduce speed and the cone on the end of a refuelling hose?
Drogue

84. In which county was the Mildenhall Treasure found?
Suffolk

85. Which periodical was first published by Ebenezer Landells and Mark Lemon? *Punch*

86. Who played Josiah Cole in the TV series *A Respectable Trade*? **Warren Clarke**

87. Was a sangrado a quack doctor, a stone fortification or a red textile? **A quack doctor**

88. What does a mysophobe fear? **Dirt**

89. What is a pelerine? **A fur cape**

90. Which book and film were based on Operation Mincemeat in 1943? *The Man Who Never Was*

91. Which American record company was founded by Berry Gordy? **Motown**

92. In gambling, what are 'Fulhams' or 'Fullhams'?
Loaded dice

93. Megass is left after – what – has been extracted?
Sugar (from cane)

94. Who hosted the TV programme *Through the Keyhole*?
David Frost

95. What was unusual about Billy Minter's scoring of 7 goals in an FA Cup tie in 1922?
His side (St Albans) lost 8-7 (to Dulwich)!

96. In which Paul Gallico story does Paul Rhayader, a crippled artist, live on the edge of the great Essex Marsh? ***The Snow Goose***

97. Who had a No 1 hit in 1988 with *Don't Turn Around*? **Aswad**

98. Is a turbit an extract from the Apocrypha, a breed of pigeon or a Canadian hat? **A breed of pigeon**

99. Whose short stories appeared in *Cabbages and Kings*, *The Four Million* and *Opinions*? **O Henry's**

100. When the blessings and evils flew out of Pandora's box what was left behind? **Hope**

Quiz 13

1. Which historical character did Alec Guinness play in the film *The Mudlark*? **Disraeli**

2. Which performer, composer of the 'Blue Yodel' songs, was the first country music recording star? **Jimmie Rodgers**

3. In which country is the major company PDVSA based? **Venezuela**

4. In which US state is Atlantic City? **New Jersey**

5. Who created the detective Reginald Fortune? **H C Bailey**

6. True or false: women have more ribs than men? **False (They have the same number)**

7. Which Channel 5 serial featured the Hart family? ***Family Affairs***

8. Where did England and South Africa play their first Test Match for 30 years in 1995? **Pretoria**

9. Who had Top Ten hits with *I Can't Stand the Rain* and *One Way Ticket*? **Eruption**

10. Is a revetment a priest's garment, a complete re-write of a manuscript or a facing of stones or concrete? **A facing of stones or concrete**

11. Which TV series, starring Jimmy Jewel, was a drama with the music of the music-hall in the 1920s and 1930s? ***Funny Man***

12. Which word means observation, intimation of termination of an agreement and a review of a play? **Notice**

13. In the film *Ace Ventura – Pet Detective* who or what was Snowflake? **A dolphin**

14. Which country did China invade in 1950? **Tibet**

15. Which planet has the Great Red Spot? **Jupiter**

16. Who was Mohammad Reza Pahlavi? **(Last) Shah of Iran**

17. Which country calls itself Matanitu Ko Viti? **Fiji**

18. To what does the adjective nundinal refer? **Fairs and markets**

19. How were prisoners executed in notade: garrotted, drowned or dismembered? **Drowned**

20. What would a gnomoloist collect? **Sayings, maxims**

21. Which word means to kill an animal for meat as prescribed by Muslim law? **Halal**

22. In heraldry, what are described as invected, embattled, engrailed, and indented? **Lines**

23. Which Spanish painter was known for his 'estilo vaporoso' and was first Director of the Seville Academy? **Murillo**

24. Buffalo and Toledo are at opposite ends of which of the Great Lakes? **Lake Erie**

25. Who wrote *The Bondman*, *The Deemster* and *The Manxsman*? **Hall Caine**

26. What name was given to two copper hemispheres (devised by von Guericke) from which, after being joined, the air could be extracted to demonstrate the effect of air pressure? **Magdeburg hemispheres**

27. Who wrote the music for the spoof documentary *The Rutles*? **Neil Innes**

28. In the film *High Noon* who was coming to kill Will Kane? **Frank Miller**

29. What has phases, Apsides and Nodes? **The moon**

30. Where would you find a jerkin-head? **On a building**

31. How many quavers have the same value as one semibreve? **8**

32. Which English city was known as Sorviodunum by the Romans? **Salisbury**

33. Who, in 1996, became the first Briton to walk alone and unaided to the South Pole? **David Hempleman-Adams**

34. In law what is a messuage: a building, a fine imposed for contempt or seizure of goods by bailiffs? **A building**

35. Which word describes circles that have a common centre? **Concentric**

36. True or false: wasps do not produce honey? **True**

37. Who were Clotho, Atropos and Lachesis? **The Fates**

38. What is the name of the heroic dog in the novel *Call of the Wild*? **Buck**

39. Who had Top Ten hits with *Groovy Train* and *All Together Now*? **Farm**

40. In which TV series did David Hasselhoff have an intelligent car? ***Knight Rider***

41. Who played Columbo in the James Bond film *For Your Eyes Only*? **Topol**

42. Who was the first Prime Minister of Russia? **Lenin**

43. Who succeeded Jack Charlton as manager of the Republic of Ireland football team? **Mick McCarthy**

44. Is a koan a New Zealand parrot, an ornamental plant or a problem with no logical answer? **A problem with no logical answer**

45. Who connects Australia (1930), Tokyo (1932) and the Cape of Good Hope (1936)? **Amy Johnson**

46. Which system of determining age was introduced by Professor Willard Frank Libby? **Radiocarbon dating**

47. Which word means a set of stairs, escape and a journey in an aircraft? **Flight**

48. What sign is given to goods approved by the BSI? **The kitemark**

49. Which word can precede feeling, founded, tempered and timed? **Ill**

50. Which was the first Rugby League Club to win the Stones Super League? **St Helen's**

51. Which Scottish comedian had a TV series called *Scotch and Wry*? **Rikki Fulton**

52. Which of these is NOT a Duke: Beaufort, Downshire, Bedford or Hamilton? **Downshire**

53. Traditionally, which fruit are not fit to pick after Michaelmas Day? **Blackberries**

54. True or false: the UK has no National Day? **True**

55. Who wrote *Payment Deferred*, *Brown On Resolution* and *The Gun*? **C S Forester**

56. Name the presenter of the TV series *The House Detectives*. **Juliette Morris**

57. Who would receive a jointure?
A widow (Settlement estate)

58. In which county was W H Hudson's *A Shepherd's Life* set? **Wiltshire**

59. Which epitaph was on the gravestone of James Bond's wife? **We have all the time in the world**

60. What was the No 1 hit by Jet Harris and Tony Meehan in 1963? ***Diamonds***

61. Which word means to render aid, an ambassador and the pastor of a church? **Minister**

62. Who wrote the verse play *The Lady's Not For Burning*?
Christopher Fry

63. For what is the town of Honiton particularly famous?
Lace

64. Is a nandine Indian bread, a cat-like animal or a water spirit? **A cat-like animal**

65. Which war was ended by the Treaties of Paris and Hubertusburg? **Seven Years War**

66. Who was the first woman to ride in the Derby?
Alex Greaves

67. In Egyptian mythology what name was given to the double of the personality which survived death? **Ka**

68. Who played the lead in the TV series *My Wonderful Life*?
Emma Wray

69. Which country was ruled by the Rurik dynasty for seven centuries? **Russia**

70. Who played Hercule Poirot in the film *Evil Under the Sun*? **Peter Ustinov**

71. Is a karoo a parrot, a Zulu cloak or a plateau? **A plateau**

72. What was the former name of Belarus? **Byelorussia**

73. Which American singer was originally known as Ruth Jones? **Dinah Washington**

74. Who played Dr Benton in the TV series *ER*?
Eriq La Salle

75. Which rugby club did Rob Andrew leave to join Newcastle? **Wasps**

76. What happened in Germany on Black Friday in 1927?
The economy collapsed

77. Is huckaback a type of cloth, a fish stew or a children's game? **Type of cloth**

78. What is an eyot? **A small island in a river or lake**

79. Is gumbo a type of soil, a coarse-grained rock or a form of bitumen? **Type of soil**

80. Give the nationality of the pop singer Jinny. **Italian**

81. Which word means a small pile of hay, a small boat and a regulating valve? **Cock**

82. Who wrote *The Vampire In Europe, The History of Witchcraft* and *The Werewolf*? **Montague Summers**

83. What space record is held by Anna Fisher?

First mother in space

84. On which British island is Sumburgh Head?   **Shetland**

85. Who played Doris Day's husband in the film *Move Over, Darling*?   **James Garner**

86. True or false: Rio de Janeiro is more than 6,000 miles from London by air?   **False (5745)**

87. Who played Kid Curry in the TV series *Alias·Smith and Jones*?   **Ben Murphy**

88. At which game were Max Euwe, Olga Rubtsova and Xie Jun World champions?   **Chess**

89. Which motorway runs from Coventry to Leicester?   **M69**

90. What would you find on a vernicle: a Latin inscription, a picture of Christ's face or a Hebrew symbol?

A picture of Christ's face

91. Is a hydrophane an opal, a mine-sweeping device or a sea-snake?   **An opal**

92. Which US state called itself Old Dominion for a while?

Virgina

93. In James Joyce's *Ulysses,* what was the name of Leopold Bloom's wife?   **Molly**

94. What word can follow Australian, Boston, Norfolk, Skye and Yorkshire?   **Terrier**

95. In which film did Paul Henreid light two cigarettes and give one to Bette Davis?   *Now, Voyager*

96. After an experiment at Leicester, where did the first local radio station open in 1970?   **Bristol**

97. What was the name of the stepped pyramidal towers in ancient Mesopotamia?   **Ziggurats**

98. Who created the spinster detective Miss Maud Silver?

Patricia Wentworth

99. Which game was formerly known as mintonette?

Volleyball

100. Where would you usually find a numnah?

Under a saddle (to prevent chafing)

Quiz 14

1. Which weapon was designed and developed by Uziel Gal?

Uzi submachine gun

2. Who played the female lead in the film *The Long Kiss Goodnight*?   **Geena Davis**

3. Who wrote *Outbreak of Love, A Difficult Young Man* and *The Cardboard Crown*?   **Martin Boyd**

4. In which TV series did Michael Elphick and Angela Thorne play flat-sharing in-laws?   *Three Up, Two Down*

5. In which country did the Moros, Muslim tribes, wage war with the Americans for 12 years?   **The Philippines**

6. Who commanded the US Pacific fleet after the attack on Pearl Harbor?   **Chester Nimitz**

7. What were transported in wardians?   **Delicate plants**

8. Who lost 6-0, 6-1 to Billie Jean King in the 1975 Wimbledon Ladies Singles Final?

Evonne Goolagong Cawley

9. Off which country's coast is the Bay of Plenty?

New Zealand's

10. Who had Top Ten hits with *Venus In Blue Jeans, Go Away Little Girl* and *Senses Working Overtime*?

Mark Wynter

11. Who began his political career as a Conservative MP, became an Independent and then a Labour Cabinet Minister and later founded two political parties?

Oswald Mosley

12. Of what is nomology the science? **Law**

13. True or false: the Original Dixieland Jazz Band was an all-white jazz band? **True**

14. In which TV dramatisation of a John Fowles novel did Laurence Oliver and Toyah Wilcox appear?

The Ebony Tower

15. In which film did Anthony Hopkins believe his dead daughter was reincarnated in a little girl called Ivy?

Audrey Rose

16. During the French Revolution you might have used an assignat: what was it? **Paper money**

17. Which country won 244 of the 281 gold medals at the 1932 Olympics? **USA**

18. In *Psycho* what was Norman Bates' hobby? **Taxidermy**

19. In which country was Al Jolson born? **Russia**

20. Who had Top Ten hits with *Straight Up*, *Opposites Attract* and *Rush Rush*? **Paula Abdul**

21. Name the teenage witch played on TV by Melissa Joan Hart. **Sabrina**

22. What is cacography? **Bad spelling or bad writing**

23. Who wrote *The Girls of Slender Means*, *Loitering With Intent* and *The Comforters*? **Muriel Spark**

24. Which word means a decimal mark, a trait or characteristic and a tip? **Point**

25. What do you do if you 'plough the sands'?
Waste your time, work uselessly

26. Which pianist-singer wrote *Ain't Misbehavin'* and *Honeysuckle Rose*? **'Fats' Waller**

27. True or false: food-rationing ended in Britain in 1952?
False (1954)

28. Is a dividivi a monkey, a tropical tree or an Australian lizard? **A tropical tree**

29. Which metals combine to form the alloy Prince's metal?
Zinc and copper

30. Whose Top Ten hits included *Poison Arrow* and *The Look of Love*? **ABC**

31. In which TV series was Julie Walters married to Alun Armstrong, and Robert Lindsay played Billy Bowman?
Brazen Hussies

32. How many plane sides has an icosahedron? **20**

33. Who was TUC General Secretary from 1960 to 1969?
George Woodcock

34. True or false: the British Lions Rugby Union team were unbeaten on their 1974 tour of South Africa? **True**

35. Which famous fictitious character was wounded at the Battle of Maiwand? **Dr Watson**

36. To an Australian, what is a kylie? **A boomerang**

37. In which Ponchielli opera is *The Dance of the Hours*?
La Gioconda

38. What, in North America, was a sagamore?
A Red Indian chief

39. Which famous greyhound was reared by Father Martin Brophy? **Mick the Miller**

40. What did Georges de Mestral invent after wondering why burrs stuck to his trousers? **Velcro**

41. Who took over the gardening column in *Radio Times* after Geoff Hamilton died? **Alan Titchmarsh**

42. 'Fumette' is the smell of what?
Game or meat when 'high'

43. What 'royal'-sounding name is given to the purer mass of metal that sinks to the bottom during smelting? **Regulus**

44. Does a steatopygous person eat only fish, have fat buttocks or live as a recluse? **Have fat buttocks**

45. Of which mystical kingdom, created by Alan Garner, was Malebron the king? **Elidor**

46. Name the famous daughter of writer Vera Brittain.
Shirley Williams

47. Which Scottish World Champion boxer was found dead in a Glasgow gutter in 1946? **Benny Lynch**

48. Who would be interested in a racloir: a croupier, an archaeologist or a mathematician?
An archaeologist (It is a flint implement)

49. Who was the original presenter of the TV programme *The Real Holiday Show*? **Gaby Roslin**

50. What was the business of Gruff & Tackleton in *The Cricket On The Hearth*? **Toy-makers**

51. Who directed the films *The Big Parade*, *The Champ* and *The Fountainhead*? **King Vidor**

52. What are lills? **Small pins**

53. Who had Top Twenty hits with *Tommy Gun*, *Bankrobber* and *Rock the Casbah*? **The Clash**

54. True or false: Blue Mantle is an official in the House of Commons? **False (A member of the College of Heralds)**

55. Whom did John Betjeman succeed as Poet Laureate?
C Day Lewis

56. Who, in a film, was *The Man Who Haunted Himself*?
Roger Moore

57. In *Twelfth Night* who is Sir Toby's foolish friend?
Sir Andrew Aguecheek

58. In which ship did the Japanese sign their surrender at the end of World War II? **USS *Missouri***

59. Who was Perry Mason's secretary? **Della Street**

60. Who played the title role in the film *My Cousin Vinny*?
Joe Pesci

61. Who played Gus Hedges in TV's *Drop the Dead Donkey*?
Robert Duncan

62. Which England Test batsman was described as the only player to call his partner for a run and wish him good luck at the same time? **Dennis Compton**

63. Which theatre was inherited by racing-driver Sheila Van Damm? **The Windmill Theatre**

64. Which surname is shared by an English actress and politician, an American gospel singer and an American Confederate general? **Jackson**

65. Which famous person was played by Robert Downey Jr in a 1991 Richard Attenborough film? **Charlie Chaplin**

66. Who loved Bess, 'the landlord's black-eyed daughter', in a famous poem by Alfred Noyes? **The highwayman**

67. In which 1951 film was Earth threatened by Zira and Bellus? **When Worlds Collide**

68. Which duo had hits with *Under Your Thumb* and *Wedding Bells*? **Godley and Creme**

69. Give the surname of Karl, Susan, Libby, Malcolm and Billy in TV's *Neighbours*. **Kennedy**

70. Whom do Americans call 'wetbacks'? **Illegal immigrants from Mexico**

71. As what did Emmett Kelly achieve fame: an artist, a baseball player or a clown? **A clown**

72. Who won 'The Mile of the Millennium' in Dublin in 1958? **Herb Elliott**

73. Who co-founded CND with Canon Collins? **Bertrand Russell**

74. Who played Cole Porter in the film *Night and Day*? **Cary Grant**

75. Which coin ceased to be legal tender in Britain on January 1st, 1961? **The farthing**

76. Who composed *Jesu, Joy of Man's Desiring*? **Bach**

77. Is an estrade a raised platform, a pass in bullfighting or an old card game? **A raised platform**

78. Which is the world's smallest state? **The Vatican**

79. What was handed over to Scotland on St Andrew's Day, 1996? **The Stone of Scone**

80. Which writer wrote King George V's Christmas Day broadcast speech (the first) in 1932? **Rudyard Kipling**

81. Who wrote *Myra Breckinridge*, *Lincoln* and *Julian*? **Gore Vidal**

82. Which record by Police went straight into the charts at No 1 in 1981? ***Don't Stand So Close To Me***

83. What was the name of Denise and Ken's son in *Coronation Street*? **Daniel**

84. What nickname was given to James Young who experimented with a distillation of oil from coal and shale? **'Paraffin'**

85. What word is used in design criticism to describe work of a tasteless, gross and foolish sort? **Kitsch**

86. Complete this literary band: William, Ginger, Douglas and ...? **Henry**

87. In TV's *Up Pompeii*, which character was played by Jeanne Mockford? **Senna the Soothsayer**

88. Which sport was played by Joe Namath? **American football**

89. Who was widowed by the death of Francis II of France? **Mary, Queen of Scots**

90. What name is given to an extravagant flourish after a signature (originally to prevent forgery): a cadenza, a queue or a paraph? **A paraph**

91. Which singer-songwriter appeared in the film *To Have and Have Not*? **Hoagy Carmichael**

92. Who slew Macbeth in Shakespeare's play? **Macduff**

93. Who wrote the book *The Color Purple*? **Alice Walker**

94. On whose last years was the film *Dance With a Stranger* based? **Ruth Ellis**

95. Which bandleader married Betty Grable? **Harry James**

96. Which word means a thicket, a heavy harrow and a checking appliance? **Brake**

97. When was the tie-break introduced into tennis: 1970, 1972 or 1974? **1970**

98. Who played the Duke of Wellington in the 1971 film *Waterloo*? **Christopher Plummer**

99. Who wrote *Clock Without Hands, The Heart Is a Lonely Hunter* and *The Member of the Wedding*?
Carson McCullers

100. Who had a No 1 hit with *D-I-V-O-R-C-E*?
Billy Connolly

Quiz 15

1. In which US state are St Petersburg, Naples, Brighton, Venice and Melbourne? **Florida**

2. Who wrote the TV series *Only Fools and Horses*?
John Sullivan

3. Which vitamin is also called retinol? **Vitamin A**

4. If you had a kanoon would you spend it, wear it or play it? **Play it (It is a dulcimer)**

5. What were passed in 1832, 1867 and 1884 to enlarge the electorate and change the constitution of the House of Commons? **The Reform Acts**

6. Whose Top Ten hits included *Gambler, Angel* and *Dear Jessie*? **Madonna's**

7. Which word means an opening in a wall or floor, emerge from the egg or to mark with close parallel lines? **Hatch**

8. Name the mother of Lady Sarah Chatto.
Princess Margaret

9. Which saint's reliquary casket was sold at Sotheby's in 1996 but prevented from leaving the country?
St Thomas à Becket's

10. In legend, from where did the Seven Sleepers come?
Ephesus

11. In America what name was given to the granite boulder onto which the Pilgrim Fathers stepped ashore in 1620?
Plymouth Rock

12. Which golfer became the youngest ever winner of the US Masters in 1997? **Tiger Woods**

13. Who calls a soldier a 'guffy'? **A sailor!**

14. Which one word means a freshwater fish, an upward curve at the foot of a square sail and the butt of a cannabis cigarette? **Roach**

15. What was the theme of the films *Violent Saturday*, *The League of Gentlemen* and *Dog Day Afternoon*?
A bank robbery

16. Who wrote *Three Go Back*, *The Lost Trumpet* and *Sunset Song*? **Lewis Grassic Gibbon**

17. On which insects would you find a scopa?
Bees (hairs on legs for carrying pollen)

18. Dai Francis, Tony Mercer and John Boulter all starred in which long-running BBC TV music show?
The Black and White Minstrels

19. Who got *Piano Medley 114* into the Top Twenty?
Charlie Kunz

20. Is roche moutonnée a glaciated rock, a braided cord or a cheese? **Glaciated rock**

21. What is the first term of the Law Year called? **Hilary**

22. In *Pride and Prejudice* what was Mr Darcy's Christian name? **Fitzwilliam**

23. Is an Ignorantine an intellectual concerned with only one topic, a piece of rounded quartz or a member of a Roman Catholic order?   **A member of a Roman Catholic order**

24. What was cut adrift in the Bay of Biscay en route to London?   **Cleopatra's Needle**

25. In which branch of medicine were Monro Primus and Monro Secundus famous?   **Anatomy**

26. What does a multicavous object have a lot of?   **Holes**

27. True or false: Scout Association HQ is at Baden-Powell House in London?   **True**

28. Who was the first boxer to win back the World Heavyweight Title?   **Floyd Patterson**

29. Which Oscar-winning actor said: ''I have a face like the behind of an elephant''?   **Charles Laughton**

30. Who played the title role in the TV series *Boyd QC*?   **Michael Denison**

31. Which title was held in Germany by English kings George I and George II?   **Elector of Hanover**

32. In medicine what does helcology specifically deal with?   **Ulcers**

33. Who had Top Twenty hits with *Womankind* and *Ten Miles High*?   **Little Angels**

34. Who succeeded George Woodcock as TUC General Secretary?   **Vic Feather**

35. In which book did Zaphod Beetlebrox appear?   ***The Hitch-Hiker's Guide To the Galaxy***

36. Who directed the films *Sergeant York*, *The Big Sleep*, *Rio Bravo* and *Red River*?   **Howard Hawks**

37. What form of transport is a palanquin?
A litter or couch carried by men

38. In heraldry, what word describes the colour of St Andrew's cross? **Argent**

39. Which bird is known as the yowley?
The yellow-hammer

40. Which country, discovered by Pedro Cabral in 1500, has mountain ranges called Serra do Mar, Serra da Mantiqueira and Serra do Espinhaço? **Brazil**

41. Which team did Bill Shankly say was the second best team in England? **Liverpool Reserves!**

42. Who, during the French Revolution, was the 'Widow Capet'? **Marie Antionette**

43. Who created Batman? **Bob Kane**

44. Which film star was nicknamed 'The Hunk'?
Victor Mature

45. In literature, whose Aunt Dahlia lived at Brinkley Court, Worcestershire? **Bertie Wooster's**

46. Who played Mr Swindley in *Coronation Street*?
Arthur Lowe

47. Who was the first US President to die in office?
William H Harrison

48. What was Terry Lightfoot's band called?
New Orleans Jazzmen

49. Is slickenside a polished rock surface produced by friction, a type of Dutch beer or a condemned pig carcass?
A polished rock surface

50. When Prince Charles was invested as Prince of Wales, who was Constable of Caenarvon Castle?
Lord Snowdon

51. Which President of the European Commission addressed the 1995 TUC Conference in Brighton?   **Jacques Santer**

52. As what was Sergei Vladimirovich Ilyushin famous?
An aircraft designer

53. Who sang in the film *Footlight Parade,* was Philip Marlowe in *Murder My Sweet* and directed *Split Second*?
Dick Powell

54. Which British football team became the first (1978) to have an all-seat stadium in Britain?   **Aberdeen**

55. What colour is a female blackbird?   **Brown**

56. Which comedian signed off "Goodnight Mrs Calabash, wherever you are."?   **Jimmy Durante**

57. Who had Top Twenty hits with *No More Mr Nice Guy, Symphony of Destruction* and *Skin o' My Teeth*?
Megadeth

58. Who wrote the play *Back To Methuselah*?
George Bernard Shaw

59. During which military campaign did landings take place at Gaba Tepe and Suvla Bay?   **Gallipoli**

60. True or false: Lee Marvin never won an Oscar?
False (He won one for *Cat Ballou)*

61. Of which group is the Duke of York an admiral?
Sea Cadet Corps

62. What was the surname of Henry IV?   **Bolingbroke**

63. When did the £1,000 note cease to be legal tender: 1930, 1940 or 1945?   **1945**

64. Is an opah a Malay manservant, a fish or a fruit of the peach family?   **A fish**

65. Early Spider, Late Spider, Ghost, Monkey and Fen are species of which flower? **Orchid**

66. Who trained Torvill and Dean? **Betty Calloway**

67. Which of these actors was NOT knighted: Donald Wolfit, John Mills, Herbert Marshall or Anthony Quayle? **Herbert Marshall**

68. In the novel *1984* for which organisation did Julia work? **Ministry of Truth**

69. Of what is catoptrics the science? **Reflected light**

70. On TV, which alien came to Boulder City? **Mork**

71. What is the assay mark for platinum? **An orb**

72. Which entertainer created Sam Small and the Ramsbottom family? **Stanley Holloway**

73. Who played a sailor in the films *The Gift Horse*, *The Sand Pebbles* and *In Which We Serve*? **Richard Attenborough**

74. Which of these animals has the longest gestation period: goat, pig or dog? **Goat**

75. In *Little Women* what did the March girls call their mother? **Marmee**

76. Which word means a series of games, a masseur and an eraser? **Rubber**

77. In which city was the 1976 TV series *Gangsters* set? **Birmingham**

78. Who duetted with RuPaul on the 1994 Top Ten hit *Don't Go Breaking My Heart*? **Elton John**

79. Which British Olympic competitor said in 1988: "Everybody back home thinks I'm crazy. They're probably right."? **'Eddie the Eagle' Edwards**

80. Who was the only British monarch of the House of Saxe-Coburg and Gotha? **Edward VII**

81. For what kind of stunt in the 1920s was Alvin 'Shipwreck' Kelly famous? **Flagpole sitting**

82. Until 1997 what happened in the House of Commons between 3:15 and 3:30 pm every Tuesday and Thursday? **Prime Minister's Question Time**

83. In which Shakespeare play does Duke Orsino appear? ***Twelfth Night***

84. Which country's legislature is called the Folketing? **Denmark's**

85. Who are trained at the College of the Propaganda? **Missionary priests**

86. Who played the lead in the films *Tickle Me, Harem Scarem, Spinout* and *Charro*? **Elvis Presley**

87. Who played Lillie Langtry in the 1978 TV series *Lillie*? **Francesca Annis**

88. What is the name of the flax ball used by Polynesian women in ceremonial dances? **Poi**

89. What was the surname of the three brothers who played for Southampton Football Club in 1988? **Wallace**

90. What was the title of the Simpsons' No 1 hit in 1991? ***Do the Bartman***

91. Who played private eye Hazell on TV? **Nicholas Ball**

92. Where is the World Bank located? **Washington**

93. Which river has Newport at its head and Cowes at its mouth? **River Medina**

94. Complete this quartet of Isaac: Michael, Hugh, John and ...? **Dingle (Foot)**

95. Which fruit did Captain Shaddock introduce to the West Indies in the 17th century? **Shaddock!**

96. Who, with two companions, held the bridge over the Tiber against the army of Lars Porsena? **Horatius**

97. Which racehorse-owner withdrew all his horses from England after his horse Allysa tested positive in 1990? **Aga Khan**

98. Which detective has been played in films by Langhorne Burton, George Curzon, David Farrar and Geoffrey Toone? **Sexton Blake**

99. Which TV family lived at 518 Crestview Drive in Los Angeles? **Beverley Hillbillies**

100. Which of the Livery Companies is first in order of civic precedence? **Mercers**

Quiz 16

1. What is added to wine to make caudle, a drink once used for invalids? **Eggs**

2. Where is Lantern FM Radio Station located? **Bideford**

3. Cabinda is an enclave of which African country? **Angola**

4. Who had Top Ten hits with *Something Good*, *Believe In Me* and *What Can You Do For Me*? **Utah Saints**

5. Who broke Bob Beamon's long-jump record? **Mike Powell**

6. Who eloped with Rachel Wardle in *The Pickwick Papers*? **Alfred Jingle**

7. Who played the lead in the TV series *The Invaders*? **Roy Thinnes**

8. Which word means a kind of seagull, a cage for hawks and to whine or whimper? **Mew**

9. What is mule-twist? **A yarn**

10. In the film *Above Us The Waves* what was the target of the midget submarines? **The *Tirpitz***

11. Ludwig II of Bavaria built a castle especially to stage the operas of which composer? **Wagner**

12. Which horse won the Derby, the Irish Derby and the King George VI and Queen Elizabeth Stakes in 1981? **Shergar**

13. What was the name of the character played by Paul Brinegar in the TV series *Rawhide*? **Wishbone**

14. Who lived among his villagers disguised as a dog in *The Dog Beneath the Skin*? **Sir Francis Crewe**

15. The island of Penang is off the coast of which country? **Malaysia**

16. In which county are the Lost Gardens of Heligan? **Cornwall**

17. Which word means froth or scum, to turn the edge over and an amount of paper? **Ream**

18. In Greece and Egypt, what is a nome? **A province**

19. Is a hoiho a Maori weapon, a species of penguin or a Hawaiian dish? **A species of penguin**

20. Of which Prime Minister did Daniel O'Connell say: "His smile was like the silver plate on a coffin." – Pitt, Peel or Palmerston? **Peel**

21. In Norse mythology, which plant caused the death of Baldur, the god of youth? **Mistletoe**

22. Which book by Helen Hanff was made into a film starring Anne Bancroft and Anthony Hopkins?
84 Charing Cross Road

23. Who presented the children's TV series *Dappledown Farm*? **Brian Cant**

24. True or false: the largest pyramid, by volume, was built by the Toltecs? **True**

25. Is a sterlet a sturgeon, a young starling or a medieval weapon? **A sturgeon**

26. Which aid for the blind began in 1928 at Vevey in Switzerland? **Guide dogs**

27. Who in 1984 became the first batsman to score centuries in his first three Test Matches? **Mohammad Azharuddin**

28. Which supertanker ran aground near Milford Haven in 1996? **Sea Empress**

29. Who was the first painter to exhibit a Cubist painting: Picasso, Braque or Gris? **Braque**

30. In what year did the Berlin Airlift begin: 1948, 1949 or 1950? **1948**

31. What were stevenographs? **Silk pictures**

32. What relationship was Joe Gargery to Pip in *Great Expectations*? **Brother-in-law**

33. Which prophetess was born in 1488 and baptized as Ursula Southiel? **Mother Shipton**

34. Is a pulka a Zulu drinking vessel, a Lapland sleigh or an African antelope? **A Lapland sleigh**

35. In the TV series *Dad's Army* why was Private Pike turned down for military service? **His blood type was too rare**

36. Which prize is awarded to the best film at the Berlin Film Festival? **Golden Bear**

37. Who wrote *Peace With God*, *World Aflame* and *Angels*? **Billy Graham**

38. Lord Byron the poet was the 6th Baron Byron of which northern town? **Rochdale**

39. On which island are Morondava, Mangoro, Mananara and Morombe? **Madagascar**

40. Who stormed Buckingham Palace on May 22nd, 1914? **Suffragettes**

41. Which lake is the source of the River Niagara? **Lake Erie**

42. Which word can mean the walrus, the clasp of a cope and a telegraph? **Morse**

43. From which family coat of arms is the pawnbrokers' sign believed to derive? **Medici**

44. Who were the first team to beat Spurs in an FA Cup Final? **Coventry City**

45. Who played the title role in the film *Clive of India*? **Ronald Colman**

46. Which comedian said: "The trouble with Freud is that he never played the Glasgow Empire Saturday night."? **Ken Dodd**

47. Who is missing from this Enid Blyton quintet: Timmy, Anne, George, Dick and . . .? **Julian**

48. Who wrote *Come and Go*, *Malone Dies* and *Happy Days*? **Samuel Beckett**

49. What is ruth? **Mercy, compassion**

50. Which famous *Tonight* reporter was known for his beard and tweed hat? **Fyfe Robertson**

51. Who played the female lead in the *Terminator* films? **Linda Hamilton**

52. In *Kidnapped* where did Ebenezer Balfour live? **The House of Shaws**

53. Who is the patron saint of postal workers and radio workers? **St Gabriel**

54. Is teucrium a metal, a German winery or a plant? **Plant (a germander)**

55. Which profession was central to the TV series *This Life*? **Legal profession**

56. True or false: almonds have more calories than chips? **True**

57. By what name was baseball player and manager Cornelius McGillicuddy known? **Connie Mack**

58. Which British film was released in the USA as *Young Scarface*? **Brighton Rock**

59. Which London museum originally opened as the Museum of Ornamental Art in 1852? **Victoria and Albert Museum**

60. In the Channel Islands, what is a vergee? **A measure of land**

61. At which observatory was the Hale telescope installed in 1948? **Mount Palomar**

62. What is used to divine the future in hepatoscopy? **An animal's liver**

63. Which film producer and entrepeneur flew round the world in a plane called *The New York Fair* in 1938? **Howard Hughes**

64. Which literary ghost wore a chain made of steel ledgers, deeds, purses and cash boxes, keys and padlocks?
Marley's ghost (In *A Christmas Carol*)

65. Which TV series featured characters surnamed Salinger and called Julia, Claudia, Bailey and Charlie?
Party of Five

66. Which European nation won two gold medals for men's judo in the 1996 Olympics: Hungary, France or Poland?
France

67. Which English philosopher and scientist was known as 'Doctor Mirabilis'? **Roger Bacon**

68. Which creatures suffer from malanders: sheep, pigs or horses? **Horses**

69. Off which country's coast is the Joseph Bonaparte Gulf?
Australia's

70. What is the Italian equivalent of the Tour de France?
Giro d'Italia

71. Which Hitchcock film featured an assassination among umbrellas, a gripping moment in a windmill and an aircraft shot down into the sea? ***Foreign Correspondent***

72. In which country is a Boys Festival celebrated by flying kites depicting carp? **Japan**

73. Who designed the first petrol-driven car? **Karl Benz**

74. Name the presenter of the TV series *Taste of the Times*.
Sophie Grigson

75. Who was Colonel Oliver North's secretary? **Fawn Hall**

76. Who created the detective Sgt Richard Cuff?
Wilkie Collins

77. Who ruled Japan until 1567? **The Shoguns**

78. Who was the first British golfer to win the US Masters?
Sandy Lyle

79. Which film starred basketball player Michael Jordan and Bugs Bunny? *Space Jam*

80. Who was the first child to be born to a reigning British monarch in the 20th century? **Prince Andrew**

81. In which Dickens novel do Charley Bates, Noah Claypole and Mr Sowerberry appear? *Oliver Twist*

82. Courgettes, squashes, gourds and pumpkins belong to which plant family? **Marrow**

83. Is a gallinazo a Spanish dance, an Italian pasta or an American vulture? **American vulture**

84. Which Russian novelist was reprieved at the last minute when facing execution in 1849? **Dostoevsky**

85. On which river are Sioux City, Omaha, Bismarck and St Joseph? **Missouri**

86. In Ancient Greece was a lekythos a coin, a flask or a sandal? **A flask**

87. In the test series against the West Indies in 1988, five cricketers captained England: Gatting, Emburey, Cowdrey and Gooch were four: who was the fifth? **Derek Pringle**

88. Who presented the TV series *Garden Party*?
Tom Barker

89. Which famous Briton died at Chitambo in 1873?
David Livingstone

90. Which word means a deep ditch, a gullible person and vital fluid? **Sap**

91. In which film was Will Hay last on the list of Mervyn Johns' murder victims? *My Learned Friend*

92. What is stored in a mattamore?   **Grain**

93. Whose radio presentation of *The War of the Worlds* terrified America in 1938?   **Orson Welles'**

94. Which word derives from 'twilled' cloth?   **Tweed**

95. Which country's flag consists of a white crescent and a white star on a red background?   **Turkey**

96. Would you find a squinch on a ship, in a tower or in the sea?   **In a tower (An arch)**

97. True or false: the sacred Islam monument The Dome of the Rock is in Damascus?   **False (Jerusalem)**

98. Who was the Governor of New South Wales who was deposed in the Rum Rebellion of 1808?   **William Bligh**

99. In which book by James Joyce do the twins Shem the Penman and Shaunn the Post appear?   *Finnegan's Wake*

100. What name is given to the architectural period from 1150 to 1550?   **Gothic**

Quiz 17

1. Who were Spurs' opponents in the FA Cup Final when Paul Gascoigne was stretchered off?   **Nottingham Forest**

2. Who was managing-director of BBC TV from 1968 to 1975?   **Huw Wheldon**

3. True or false: a beaver was the visor of a helmet?   **True**

4. In which island group is Guadalcanal?   **Solomon Islands**

5. Whom did Clara Padilla accuse of stealing a diamond and emerald bracelet in 1970?   **Bobby Moore**

6. If you had plotty would you drink it, see a doctor or make pottery?
Drink it (It is a mixture of wine, water and spices)

7. What shape are the sound-holes in violins?   **f-shaped**

8. Who wrote the play *Who's Afraid of Virginia Woolf*?
Edward Albee

9. Who played the submarine commander in the film *Ice Station Zebra*?   **Rock Hudson**

10. What did Sir Erasmus Wilson bring to England from Egypt in 1877?   **Cleopatra's Needle**

11. Name the presenter of TV's *TFI Friday*.   **Chris Evans**

12. Which tennis player, a Wimbledon Men's Singles finalist, was nicknamed the Chattanooga Express?
Roscoe Tanner

13. According to legend, the Scilly Isles are the only visible part of which submerged land?   **Lyonesse**

14. Petuntse is used in the manufacture of porcelain, silk or coffee?   **Porcelain**

15. Which British bandleader had the signature tune *Somebody Stole My Gal*?   **Billy Cotton**

16. Which TV comedian lived at 52 Acacia Avenue in his series?   **Harry Worth**

17. Who, in his work, would scumble?   **A painter**

18. In *David Copperfield* whose thoughts got mixed up with those of Charles I?   **Mr Dick's**

19. Which sea-creature belongs to the hippocampus genus?
The sea-horse

20. He is Efi in Israel, Aref in Egypt and Charlie in France. Who is he in Britain?   **Wally**

21. Whose only No 1 was *The Streak*? **Ray Stevens**

22. Who was the girl in the film *One Hundred Men and A Girl*? **Deanna Durbin**

23. True or false: the Tropic of Capricorn passes through Madagascar? **True**

24. In the 1936 Olympics, what did the two American high-jumpers do while waiting to jump: read newsapers, play dice or sleep? **Played dice (craps)**

25. Which word means drawing off wine from the lees? **Rack(ing)**

26. Is a quokka an Indian measure of weight, a Finnish geyser or an animal? **An animal (Bandicoot)**

27. Which modern orchestral instrument developed from the 16th Century curtal? **Bassoon**

28. Which pop duo featured on Spurs' football squad's three Top Twenty hits? **Chas and Dave**

29. Which word means the greater proportion, a church service and to concentrate in one area? **Mass**

30. Who played the title role in the 1983 film *The Wicked Lady*? **Faye Dunaway**

31. Which character did Ward Bond play in the TV series *Wagon Train*? **Seth Adams**

32. Where is the mixture orimulsion used? **In power stations**

33. Who had the first UK instrumental No 1 hit? **Mantovani and his Orchestra**

34. Who wrote *Adam Bede* and *Daniel Deronda*? **George Eliot**

35. From what was oakum, used for caulking seams and stopping leaks, derived? **Old rope**

36. Which singer, who had No 1 hits, starred in the film
Carnal Knowledge? **Art Garfunkel**

37. Which word means a small cask, a peg or bolt and an
ornamental badge with a fastening? **A pin**

38. Who was the first manager of the England football team?
Walter Winterbottom

39. Who, in *Julius Caesar,* had 'the falling sickness'?
Julius Caesar

40. Which European leader said: "My foreign policy is
'Nothing for nothing' "? **Mussolini**

41. Traditionally, which bugle-call was sounded in the Army
to recall all men to barracks? **First Post**

42. Who composed the opera *Mozart and Salieri*?
Rimsky-Korsakov

43. Which writers were portrayed in the film *Devotion*?
The Brontë sisters

44. Which long-running TV show was originally first
broadcast on New Year's Day from a converted church in
Manchester in 1964? ***Top of the Pops***

45. What is produced by a Wimshurst machine?
Static electricity

46. Of which creature is a herling the young? **Sea-trout**

47. What was David Soul's second No 1? ***Silver Lady***

48. What are you making if you carry out panification?
Bread

49. Which creatures belong to the Pulex genus? **Fleas**

50. True or false: the first European Athletic Championships
were held in Turin? **True**

51. Who had Top Twenty hits with *Wasteland*, *Tower of Strength* and *Butterfly On a Wheel*? **Mission**

52. Who succeeded Bob Paisley as Liverpool FC manager? **Joe Fagan**

53. The original Morgan sports car was developed in the school workshops of which spa town college? **Malvern**

54. Which TV series sprang out of the TV play *A Magnum For Schneider*? **Callan**

55. Which barnstorming actor appeared in the films *The Face At the Window*, *The Crimes of Stephen Hawke* and *The Greed of William Hart*? **Tod Slaughter**

56. What was Jane Morgan's only No 1 hit? **The Day the Rains Came**

57. Kalimantan forms most of which island? **Borneo**

58. Whom does Gold Stick attend? **The sovereign**

59. In the rhyme, how far is it to Babylon? **Three score miles and ten**

60. What did Edward Lear's Pobble lack? **Toes**

61. Which Roman statesman, after a defeat by Carthage, ended all his speeches with "Carthage must be destroyed."? **Cato**

62. Of which language was Linear B an early form of script? **Greek**

63. Which product was advertised on TV by Mary Holland and Lynda Bellingham? **Oxo**

64. What is the Latin for "Let there be light"? **Fiat lux**

65. If you enucleate do you cause an explosion, blink or solve something? **Solve something**

66. What is hardanger? **Decorative needlework**

67. Of whom did Henry VIII write in a letter: "This man hath the sow by the ear."? **Thomas Cranmer**

68. What term do we now use to describe the 'Old Comers'? **Pilgrim Fathers**

69. In which Otto Preminger film did Michael Caine play a saxophone when he was stressed? *Hurry Sundown*

70. Which US state forms most of the western shore of Lake Michigan? **Wisconsin**

71. In which TV series did Dr Bywaters, Dr Armstrong, Dr Parker-Brown and Sister Washington appear? *General Hospital*

72. In which country was there a ruler called a mpret? **Albania**

73. True or false: the Dutch East Indies competed in the finals of the 1954 Football World Cup? **False (but they did in 1938)**

74. What is a Tibetan monk called? **A lama**

75. Who bought Stratfield Saye, which became the family home of his descendants? **Duke of Wellington**

76. In advertising, which brand of cigarette were you never alone with? **Strand**

77. What does a twoccer do? **Steals cars**

78. Hirudin, secreted by the leech, prevents what? **Blood clotting**

79. What, in the Bible, is better than rubies? **Wisdom**

80. Which Second Division football club put its entire side up for sale in 1983? **Swansea**

81. Which game, similar to basketball, has six men and six women on each side? **Korfball**

82. From which musical do the songs *It's Nicer in Nice* and *I Could be Happy With You* come? ***The Boy Friend***

83. Who dresses up as Herne the Hunter in *The Merry Wives of Windsor*? **Falstaff**

84. Of which literary character was it said: "In this matter of shimmering into rooms the chappie is rummy to a degree."? **Jeeves**

85. True or false: the Equator passes through Java? **False**

86. Of what is oneirology the science? **Dreams**

87. Which famous building was given a steel corset in 1992?
The Leaning Tower of Pisa

88. In which children's story did Gerda search for her abducted friend, Kai? ***The Snow Queen***

89. Which British Prime Minister gave his views on other British Prime Ministers in TV's *A Prime Minister On Prime Ministers*? **Harold Wilson**

90. In what does a fell-monger deal? **Hides and skins**

91. Who composed the music for *Rigoletto*? **Verdi**

92. Who had Top Ten hits with *Farewell Is a Lonely Sound*, *It's Wonderful* and *Hold On To My Love*? **Jimmy Ruffin**

93. What happened to the tigers who stole Little Black Sambo's clothes? **They became melted butter**

94. Who was the first Irishman to win the Tour de France?
Stephen Roache

95. Which TV sheriff had four magic feathers? **Tex Tucker**

96. Where would you have once found stickers, landfalls and trackers? **On an organ**

97. Jean Tijou is regarded as the greatest craftsman in his medium ever to have worked in England: what was his medium? **Wrought iron**

98. Whose nose looks red when "icicles hang by the wall"? **Marian's**

99. Which was the first London hospital to specialise in eye diseases? **Moorfields**

100. Which wind is called libeccio? **South-west wind**

Quiz 18

1. Is a bougie an evil spirit, a small truck or a wax candle? **A wax candle**

2. In which film did John Wayne play Sergeant John M Stryker? *Sands of Iwo Jima*

3. Who owned the horse Desert Orchid? **Richard Burridge**

4. What is a sea-fox? **(A type of) Shark**

5. Which of Shakespeare's Seven Ages precedes the soldier? **The lover**

6. In which country was conductor Georg Solti born? **Hungary**

7. Which British TV show was devised by a Dutch housewife under the name *Een Van de Acht*? *The Generation Game*

8. What does the legal warrant *mittimus* literally mean? **We send**

9. Who had Top Twenty hits with *Hubble Bubble Toil and Trouble*, *Oh No, Not My Baby* and *Just Like a Woman*?
Manfred Mann

10. True or false: R A Butler was Speaker of the House of Commons? **False**

11. Which substance was used in the armed forces to whiten or colour belts, webbing, etc? **Blanco**

12. Alkanes, alkenes and alkynes are members of which group of chemical compounds? **Hydrocarbons**

13. Where would you usually see the word 'obiit'?
On a gravestone, tombstone

14. Who wrote the bestselling book *The Copper Beech*?
Maeve Binchy

15. Who had albums called *Wild Wood* and *Stanley Road*?
Paul Weller

16. What was the work of Gregory the Illuminator, Martin of Tours and Chrysostom? **They were missionaries**

17. Whose first film was *Red River* and his last was *The Defector*? **Montgomery Clift**

18. Which Australian fast bowler retired from cricket after being no-balled for throwing four times in his first over in the First Test against South Africa in 1963? **Ian Meckiff**

19. Which Shakespearean king said: "I have been studying how I may compare / This prison where I live unto the world:"? **Richard II**

20. Which city comes next in this sequence: Amsterdam, Los Angeles, Berlin, London ...?
Helsinki (Olympic venues)

21. Whose Top Twenty hits included *Mystify, Good Times* and *The Gift*? **INXS**

22. True or false: there are two cities called Niagara Falls?

True

23. Which flower is also called Lords and Ladies?

(Wild) Arum lily

24. For which performers did Haydn write the opera *Dido* in 1778? **(The Esterhazy) Marionettes (Theatre)**

25. Name the TV show presented by Ulrika Jonsson and John Fashanu. *Gladiators*

26. With what is a Hertzsprung-Russell diagram concerned?

Stars

27. What is the well-known name for the aperient composed of Rochelle salt, bicarbonate of soda and tartaric acid?

Seidlitz powder

28. Who painted *Au Lapine Agile* and *Acrobate et Jeune Arlequin*? **Picasso**

29. Which animal was revered by the Mayans? **The jaguar**

30. Which Australian won the British Open Golf championship four times between 1954 and 1965?

Peter Thomson

31. In what field was Tyrone Guthrie famous? **The theatre**

32. Where is System X used? **In telephone exchanges**

33. With what are the Midrash commentaries concerned?

The Bible

34. What part did Richard Attenborough play in the films *The Sand Pebbles, Morning Departure* and *The Gift Horse*?

A sailor

35. Where would you find cat-holes?
On a ship (They are holes that the cables go through)

36. From which creatures' bladders is isinglass prepared?

Fish

37. Which European university set up the first chemistry laboratory (in 1650)?

Leyden

38. Who played Marina in TV's *Last of the Summer Wine*?

Jean Fergusson

39. Whose films included *The Man in Grey*, *Waterloo Road* and *Soldiers Three*?

Stewart Granger

40. How far was the territorial limit from a country's coast set at by a UN convention of 1982?

12 miles

41. What is your masseter?

Muscle (raises the lower jaw)

42. What is the official religion of Sweden?

Lutheranism

43. Which of these newspapers is the oldest: *Daily Mirror*, *Daily Mail* or *Daily Express*?

Daily Mail (1896)

44. What name was given to old laws which restrained excessive individual consumption?

Sumptuary laws

45. Under what name did Eleanor Gough Mckay become famous?

Billie Holiday

46. What is congou?

(Chinese black) tea

47. Which former 1960s World Heavyweight Boxing Champion died of a drugs overdose in 1970?

Sonny Liston

48. What is ornithopily?

Pollination of flowers by birds

49. Name the presenter on TV of *Heart of the Matter*.

Joan Bakewell

50. Who or what 'piaffes'?

A horse

51. Who was the first person to meet the risen Jesus?

Mary Magdalene

52. Who had Top Twenty hits with *Rhythm Is a Mystery, So Right* and *Let Me Show You*? **K-Klass**

53. Which famous poet died of fever at Missolonghi? **Lord Byron**

54. With whom is the organisation Providence Row concerned? **Homeless people**

55. From which country does gamelan music originate? **Indonesia**

56. What is a hoggerel? **A sheep (in its 2nd year)**

57. For what do people prepare on Parasceve? **The Jewish Sabbath**

58. Who succeeded Sir Stanley Rous as President of FIFA? **João Havelange**

59. Who was ruler of Russia at the time of the American and French Revolutions? **Catherine the Great**

60. Who won the Best Actor Oscar for his portrayal of a mentally-retarded man in the film *Charly*? **Cliff Robertson**

61. Which Shropshire town holds annual Olympian Games? **Much Wenlock**

62. Is a zimocca a Himalayan goat, a type of sponge or an Egyptian hat? **Type of sponge**

63. Who played Captain Kathryn Janeway in TV's *Star Trek: Voyager*? **Kate Mulgrew**

64. Who wrote *The Edible Woman*, *Life Before Man* and *Bodily Harm*? **Margaret Atwood**

65. Which country has the lilangeni as its unit of currency: Swaziland, Tonga or Rwanda? **Swaziland**

66. With what was the TV series *Red Base One Four* concerned? **London Ambulance Service**

67. In which estuary is the Nore sandbank? **The Thames estuary**

68. What are the Hindu scriptures called? **Vedas**

69. True or false: an ounce is a 12th part of a pound troy? **True**

70. From what do bees make honey? **Nectar**

71. What kind of garment was a talma? **A cape or cloak**

72. With which painting movement were Paul Klee, Paul Nash and André Masson concerned? **Surrealism**

73. Who played Captain Peter Churchill in the film *Odette*? **Trevor Howard**

74. Which word means to melt and clarify, to apply a first coat of plaster to and to bestow or pay? **Render**

75. Who composed *Cavelleria Rusticana*? **Mascagni**

76. In which musical is Billy Bigelow the central male character? *Carousel*

77. In what position did James Hunt finish in the last Grand Prix race of 1976 which gave him the world title? **Third**

78. Name the presenter of the TV shows *Strike It Lucky* and *Strike It Rich*. **Michael Barrymore**

79. In what is a Mills Cross used: radio-astronomy, heraldry or surveying? **Radio-astronomy**

80. Who had a 1975 No 1 hit with *Tears On My Pillow*? **Johnny Nash**

81. Which honour did Lester Piggott lose when he was jailed for tax fraud? **OBE**

82. What are susi, surah and surat? **Cloth, material**

83. What was the subject of the TV series *The A Force*?
Black entertainers

84. Of which republic was Thomas Masaryk the first President? **Czechoslovakia**

85. In which country was the ancient kingdom of Ossory?
Ireland

86. Who played the female lead in the film *Paint Your Wagon*? **Jean Seberg**

87. Who had Top Ten hits with *Renta Santa* and *Bionic Santa*? **Chris Hill**

88. Which English batsman scored centuries in three successive Tests in Australia in 1987? **Chris Board**

89. Which river is spanned by the George Washington Bridge? **Hudson River**

90. Which one word can mean grip, a sitting of eggs and a connecting device in a car engine? **Clutch**

91. Which ceremonial rite was performed on Maundy Thursdays by English sovereigns until William III?
The washing of pilgrims' feet

92. Is a matamata a monkey, a goat or a turtle? **A turtle**

93. What is the capital of Lesotho? **Maseru**

94. Which musical group comprised John Lewis, Milt Jackson, Percy Heath and Kenny Clarke?
Modern Jazz Quartet

95. Which actor who played Doctor Who died in May 1996?
Jon Pertwee

96. Which regiment features in TV's *Soldier, Soldier*?
King's Own Fusiliers

97. After which battle did Mark Antony commit suicide?
Battle of Actium

98. Michael Caine failed the screen test for which character part in the film *Zulu*? **Harry Hook**

99. What does a philopolemic person like?
War, argument, controversy

100. In music, which word means the use of symbols to represent individual sounds? **Notation**

Quiz 19

1. Which British athlete broke the World Triple Jump record at the European Indoor Championships in 1998?
Ashia Hansen

2. On TV what was the name of Dr Frasier Crane's brother?
Niles

3. Which county cricket side was disqualified from the Benson and Hedges Cup by the TCCB in 1979?
Somerset

4. In which country is the Sao Francisco River? **Brazil**

5. Who played the murderer in the film *Rear Window*?
Raymond Burr

6. Who wrote *The Gods of Pegana*, *Plays of Gods* and *To Awaken Pegasus*? **Lord Dunsany**

7. Which character was played in TV's *The New Adventures of Superman* by Justin Whalin? **Jimmy Olsen**

8. Which dye sounds as if it might be more insane than the next one? **Madder!**

9. Which word means strong-smelling, lofty and acute in pitch? **High**

10. Who had a 1987 No 1 with *Star Trekkin'*? **The Firm**

11. Who is the patron saint of soldiers? **St George**

12. What is measured in barns?
Area (cross-sectional area of an atomic nucleus)

13. What was a hauberk? **A coat of mail**

14. Of which US state is Sacramento the capital? **California**

15. Who first met at Thingvellir in 930 AD?
World's oldest Parliament (in Iceland)

16. Is serein a fine silk, a fine rain or a fine silver thread?
Fine rain

17. Which part of the body is affected by ulitis? **The gums**

18. Who played Garp in the film *The World According To Garp*? **Robin Williams**

19. Who in 1980 became the first British boxer since Ted Lewis in 1917 to win a world title in the USA?
Alan Minter

20. Is tormina a bowel pain, a translucent quartz or an Italian bread? **Pain in the bowels**

21. Who played a supermarket manager in the TV series *Slinger's Day*? **Bruce Forsyth**

22. In which country are the cities of Coimbra, Braga and Setubal? **Portugal**

23. Which British industry became nationalised on January 1st, 1947? **Coal**

24. Who had Top Ten hits with *Yes My Darling Daughter* and *I Want To Stay Here*? **Eydie Gormé**

25. Who was the leader of the People's Temple religious cult?
Jim Jones

26. Who painted "old timey things . . . all from memory."?
Grandma Moses

27. In which years were there three Popes: 1958, 1968 or 1978? **1978**

28. Who wrote *The Overloaded Ark* and *Beasts In My Belfry*?
Gerald Durrell

29. What is SNOBOL? **A computer language**

30. True or false: the Coriolis Effect is to do with the moon's orbit?
False (It is the effect of the earth's rotation on objects on earth)

31. What breed of dog was cartoon character Scooby Doo?
Great Dane

32. Who composed the operettas *Frederica* and *The Count of Luxembourg*? **Franz Lehar**

33. In which country was the Emperor known as The Lion of Judah? **Ethiopia**

34. In which sport was the County Championship abandoned in 1982 after 87 years? **Rugby League**

35. Who played the ghost in the film *The Ghost and Mrs Muir*? **Rex Harrison**

36. What is the equivalent rank in the Navy of an Army Lieutenant-Colonel? **Commander**

37. Is a genipap a small monkey, a fruit or a muscle?
A fruit

38. Who wrote the books *Going For a Song*, *English Furniture* and *A Life Among Antiques*? **Arthur Negus**

39. What is the name of the dog that Garfield the cat teases?
Odie

40. Who had Top Twenty hits with *Autobahn* and *The Robots*? **Kraftwerk**

41. In the John Carpenter film *Christine* who or what was Christine? **A car**

42. Which country's king was assassinated during a state visit to France in 1934? **Yugoslavia's**

43. Who wrote *The Jungle*, *Oil* and *Boston*? **Upton Sinclair**

44. True or false: a staggard is a four-year-old stag? **True**

45. What is a telpher?
A monorail on which the vehicle travels beneath the rail

46. In which sport was Tony Hand the first British player to be drafted by a Canadian team? **Ice hockey**

47. What do Americans call a love-bite? **A hickey**

48. When would you wear salopettes? **When skiing**

49. Is a pintado a bird, a bolt or part of a leaf? **A bird**

50. With which club did Eric Cantona win his first British Championship medal? **Leeds United**

51. What was the setting for the TV series *Island*? **Jersey**

52. For what purpose are tan-balls used? **As fuel**

53. Which archaeologist excavated the royal cemetery at Ur of the Chaldees? **Sir Leonard Woolley**

54. Who wrote the boys' stories *With Moore At Corunna*, *With Roberts At Pretoria* and *With Buller In Natal*?
G A Henty

55. Is a veilleuse a hatmaker, an alarm trumpet or a night-lamp? **A night-lamp**

56. Of which country is Zealand (or Sjaelland) the main island? **Denmark**

57. In which year did the USSR break up into republics? **1991**

58. Which word means to listen to, a leaning and desire or pleasure? **List**

59. In which film did T-1000 hunt John Connor? ***Terminator 2 – Judgment Day***

60. What is GRP? **Glass-Reinforced Plastic**

61. What was Johnny Nash's No 1 hit of 1975? ***Tears On My Pillow***

62. Which provincial capital of Canada was first called Pile o' Bones in 1822? **Regina**

63. True or false: one gram of gold can be drawn into a wire one kilometre in length? **True**

64. Who govern in a gerontocracy? **Old men**

65. Name the subject of the TV series *Under the Moon*. **Sport**

66. Who was the first bishop of Lindisfarne? **Saint Aidan**

67. Who composed the opera *Salome*? **Richard Strauss**

68. Of which river is the Red River a tributary? **Mississippi**

69. On a ship, what is a vang? **A guy-rope**

70. What were *Burnt Norton*, *East Coker*, *The Dry Salvages* and *Little Gidding* collectively known as? ***The Four Quartets***

71. In which country is the kwacha the unit of currency? **Zambia**

72. What is felicide? **The killing of a cat**

73. Who was the first woman to be US Secretary of State? **Madeleine Albright**

74. Is an eagre a young hawk, a court card in whist or a river tidal wave? **River tidal wave**

75. What colour is the dye tartrazine? **Yellow**

76. In which film did Will Hay delay the signing of a vital pact by having a street band play all the national anthems of the signatories? *The Black Sheep of Whitehall*

77. Which Spanish cyclist, despite testing positive for the drug Probeneid, won the Tour de France in 1988? **Pedro Delgado**

78. In which country were the Whiteboys a secret organisation of the 18th century? **Ireland**

79. What was Donna's job in the TV series *My Wonderful Life*? **A nurse**

80. When does a vicennial event occur? **Every 20 years**

81. The Rhind papyrus, Tsu-Chung-chih, Archimedes and von Leibnitz all gave approximations of which transcendental irrational? **Pi**

82. Who had Top Twenty hits with *Blue Room* and *Little Fluffy Clouds*? **Orb**

83. In which London street did four IRA gunmen hold Mr and Mrs John Matthews hostage in 1975? **Balcombe Street**

84. Give Spike Milligan's Christian names. **Terence Alan**

85. Who formed a British political party called The New Party in 1931? **Oswald Mosley**

86. Which seabird is sometimes called the hacklet? **Kittiwake**

87. True or false: Walter Raleigh never spelled his surname R-a-l-e-i-g-h? **True**

88. What, in a castle, is the pont-levis? **The drawbridge**

89. Which was the first US state to pass prohibition laws: Maine, Oklahoma or Kansas? **Maine**

90. Who wrote *The Yellow Claw*, *Yellow Shadows* and *The Quest of the Sacred Slipper*? **Sax Rohmer**

91. Which comedy film told Virgil Starkwell's life story? ***Take the Money and Run***

92. Which word means a choice of volition, bequeath and desire or wish? **Will**

93. What was a George noble? **A gold coin**

94. Which TV series featured characters called Liz Shaw, Ian Worrell and Alan McIntyre? ***Bodyguards***

95. In which country are the Wakhan Salient, Helmand River and Lake Saberi? **Afghanistan**

96. Who had a No 1 hit in 1981 with *Under Pressure*? **Queen**

97. In which athletic event would an athlete use a Nemeth? **The javelin**

98. Which French political party was formed in 1972 by Jean-Marie Le Pen? **National Front**

99. How old is brandy or port marked VSOP? **25 years old**

100. Which famous female traveller and explorer wrote *A Winter In Arabia*, *Beyond Euphrates* and *The Coast of Incense*? **Freya Stark**

Quiz 20

1. What was the name of the probe which sent back information about Jupiter's atmosphere in 1996? **Galileo**

2. True or false: the Pamirs are an Indian people?
False (Asian plateau)

3. What was Deborah Kerr's profession in the film *Heaven Knows, Mr Allison*? **A nun**

4. Is Texel a computer language, a trade name for non-absorbent material or an island in the North Sea?
An island (in the Frisian Islands)

5. Name the actor playing Dr Mark Greene in TV's *ER*.
Anthony Edwards

6. Which sporting trophy has a figure of Abe Mitchell on its top? **The Ryder Cup**

7. In which country is Matabeleland? **Zimbabwe**

8. Who was Richard Nixon's Chief of Staff?
H R Haldeman

9. Who wrote *The Slave, Old Love, Lost in America* and *Gimpel the Fool*? **Isaac Singer**

10. Which British island did the Romans call Mona?
Anglesey

11. What did the acronym TINA – associated with Mrs Thatcher – stand for? **There is no alternative**

12. Which vitamin is also called tocopherol? **Vitamin E**

13. In religion, what is parousia? **Christ's second coming**

14. Which singer's first film was *That Midnight Kiss*?
Mario Lanza

15. In 1991, who became the first British winner of the British Women's Open Squash title since 1961? **Lisa Opie**

16. Who had Top Ten hits with *Dancing Tight*, *What Do I Do* and *I Can Prove It*? **Phil Fearon**

17. To which country did Raquel go when she left Curly in *Coronation Street*? **Malaysia**

18. What shape is a flabellate object? **Fan-shaped**

19. What kind of tree is a durmast? **An oak**

20. Who wrote *On the Road*, *Big Sur* and *Desolation Angels*? **Jack Kerouac**

21. Which national football team was hailed as 'The New Wembley Wizards' in 1953? **Hungary**

22. Was a poleyn a ferret, a piece of armour or a homeless animal? **A piece of armour**

23. In which city was a plaster figure of a 'Goddess of Democracy' raised in May 1989? **Peking (Beijing)**

24. Who wrote *Fear of Flying*? **Erica Jong**

25. Who concocted an elixir of youth in the film *Monkey Business*?
A chimpanzee (Its name was Esther and it poured the solution into the water cooler)

26. When Alan Coren and Sandy Toksvig were team captains and Bob Holness was the presenter, what was the TV programme? ***Call My Bluff***

27. Which dance, inspired by a solo flight, originated in Harlem in 1927? **The Lindy Hop**

28. Who was King of England when the 100 Years War began? **Edward III**

29. What are usually described as 'dog-eared'?

(Turned down) book pages

30. What is a mopoke or morepork? **A bird**

31. Which Shakespearean character made a speech beginning: "Romans, countrymen, and lovers! hear me for my cause"? **Brutus**

32. What was James Herriot's sequel to *All Creatures Great and Small*? ***All Things Bright and Beautiful***

33. Which capital city was named Yeda until 1868? **Tokyo**

34. From which musical do the songs *How Are Things in Glocca Morra* and *Old Devil Moon* come?

Finian's Rainbow

35. True or False: Marcus Nerva was a Roman Emperor?

True

36. Who played Mr Lucas in TV's *Are You Being Served*?

Trevor Bannister

37. Is a granadilla a fruit, a type of armadillo or a flower?

A flower

38. Who was tried by the Inquisition at Rome after publishing *A Dialogue on the Two Great Systems of the World*?

Galileo

39. Which silent film, depicting the life of an eskimo family, was written, directed, edited and photographed by Robert Flaherty? ***Nanook of the North***

40. Who was the first footballer to be transferred between two British clubs for £50,000? **Denis Law**

41. Who had hits with *Girls Just Want To Have Fun* and *She Bop*? **Cyndi Lauper**

42. From which sport was the dance, the Watusi, derived?

Surf-boarding

43. Which term was coined in 1947 after Kenneth Arnold's strange experience? **Flying saucer**

44. What is a jalousie? **A louvre blind, a shutter**

45. For his work on what is scientist Joseph Gay-Lussac best known? **Gases**

46. Who launched the idea of the Crusades? **The Pope**

47. Which Paul Anka song upset the National Organisation for Women? ***(You're) Having My Baby***

48. Who led bands called His Yale Collegians and His Connecticut Yankees? **Rudy Vallee**

49. Where have you been if you've been 'fake-baking'? **On a sunbed, in a tanning salon**

50. Who were Rowdy Roddy Piper, Ravishing Rick Rude and Sergeant Slaughter? **Professional wrestlers**

51. From which album did Michael Jackson's hit, *The Way,* come? ***Bad***

52. What kind of lettering is majuscule lettering? **Large lettering**

53. True or false: the Japanese called the hula hoop the huru hoopu? **True**

54. Who drove a Cooper-Climax to win five consecutive Grands Prix and the World Championship in 1960? **Jack Brabham**

55. What was James Cagney trying to sell to the Russians in the film *One, Two, Three*? **Coca Cola**

56. Richmond, Norfolk, Suffolk and Winchester are all in which US state? **Virginia**

57. In which mythology is Manu the first man and father of the human race? **Hindu**

58. Which singer/songwriter was formerly Bette Midler's pianist and arranger? **Barry Manilow**

59. Which US poet wrote the opera *Le Testament* and left an unfinished opera called *Cavalcanti*? **Ezra Pound**

60. In which province is Canada's capital, Ottawa? **Ontario**

61. They are Schlumpfe in Germany, Puffo in Italy and Pitufo in Spain: what do we call them? **Smurfs**

62. Which of these is the odd one out: Vancouver, Natal, Hudson Bay or the Falkland Islands?
Natal (Not named after an Englishman)

63. Who played the title role in the film *Evita*? **Madonna**

64. If the waitress shouted "Haystack" in a fast-food diner, what have you ordered? **Strawberry pancakes!**

65. By whom was Robert Clive employed when he won the Battle of Plassey? **The East India Company**

66. Name the TV series featuring the characters David Horton, Owen Newitt and Geraldine Granger.
The Vicar of Dibley

67. Which British pair won the two-man bobsled gold (with help from the Italians) in the 1964 Winter Olympics?
Tony Nash and Robin Dixon

68. Whose album brought fame to Mahlathini and the Mahotella Queens? **Neil Simon's *Graceland***

69. Which word means a hollow shaping container, a growth of fungi and loose earth? **Mould**

70. What name is given to the oval emblem containing hieroglyphic characters which name an ancient Egyptian pharaoh? **Cartouche**

71. True or false: Fred Stolle lost in three successive Men's Singles finals at Wimbledon? **True**

72. What nationality was Catherine the Great? **German**

73. Who catalogued all Mozart's works by number?
Ludwig Kochel

74. When the film *Red Dust* was remade in 1954, what was it called? *Mogambo*

75. What is japan? **A varnish**

76. Complete this quartet of Teenage Mutant Ninja Turtles: Michelangelo, Raphael, Leonardo and . . .? **Donatello**

77. During Manchester United's 5-1 defeat of Benfica in Lisbon in 1966 a spectator ran on to the field with a knife: what did he do? **Cut off a lock of George Best's hair**

78. Where did Columbus make his first landfall on his famous voyage? **The Bahamas**

79. Is a galliwasp an insect, a lizard or a small crocodile?
A lizard

80. Give the surname of Patrick and Pippa in TV's *One Foot in the Grave*. **Trench**

81. What is the name of the optical toy with a series of pictures on the inside of a cylinder which, when rotated, give the impression of movement? **Zoetrope**

82. Complete this pop group: Jon Moss, Mikey Craig, Roy Hay and . . .? **Boy George**

83. Which children's game was known in England in the 1850s as wiggle-waggle? **Simon Says**

84. With which movement was Millicent Fawcett associated?
Women's Suffrage

85. What would an Australian Aborigine carry in a magra?
A child (It is a sling)

86. In literature, where did Mrs Wiggs live?
In the Cabbage Patch (Suburb of Louisville)

87. With whom did a knight play chess in the film *The Seventh Seal*? **Death**

88. At which rock fortress were Jewish fanatics besieged by Romans in 73 AD and finally committed suicide?
Masada

89. Who was Brian Clough's famous assistant manager at several clubs? **Peter Taylor**

90. Which town, with chalybeate springs, has a famous shopping parade called The Pantiles? **Tunbridge Wells**

91. In which film did Louis Armstrong and Bing Crosby sing *Now You Has Jazz*? ***High Society***

92. Who wrote *The Prize* and *The Plot*? **Irving Wallace**

93. What was the subject of the BBC TV programme *The Terrace*? **Interior design, DIY, home decorating, etc.**

94. Which 1951 recording by Jackie Brenston and the Ike Turner Band is claimed by some to be the first rock record? ***Rocket 88***

95. Who were Aglaia, Thalia and Euphrosyne?
The Three Graces

96. Whose Symphony in G No 100 was nicknamed The Military? **Haydn's**

97. Which of these has the greatest area: Pakistan, Nigeria or Colombia? **Colombia**

98. Which was the last dynasty of China? **Manchu**

99. How many gallons make a bushel? **8**

100. Who directed the film *Prince of Tides*? **Barbra Streisand**

Quiz 21

1. What is the name of the Great Dane in the cartoon strip drawn by Brad Anderson? **Marmaduke**

2. Who was Olivia's steward in *Twelfth Night*? **Malvolio**

3. Whose headed goal won the 1980 FA Cup for West Ham United? **Trevor Brooking's**

4. What is the capital of the US state of Vermont? **Montpelier**

5. Who was the original presenter on TV's *Wish You Were Here*? **Judith Chalmers**

6. Which word means a hasty kiss, a measure for dry goods and to nip with the beak? **Peck**

7. Does razee mean to cut down the number of a ship's decks, to burn the stubble of a maize crop or to transport slaves? **To cut down the number of a ship's decks**

8. True or false: the Cyrillic alphabet was devised by St Cyril? **True**

9. Who had a 1972 hit with *The First Time Ever I Saw Your Face*? **Roberta Flack**

10. Who wrote the book *Exodus*? **Leon Uris**

11. What is the American equivalent of the British TV programme *University Challenge*? ***College Bowl***

12. Where will you find *Bel and the Dragon*, *Baruch* and *Susanna*? **In the Apocrypha**

13. Who played the title role in the 1958 film *tom thumb*? **Russ Tamblyn**

14. What sort of trees are snow gums? **Eucalyptus**

15. Which position was held by the Earl of Wilmington, Earl of Bute and Earl of Shelburne? **British Prime Minister**

16. For which famous recipe instruction from her cookery book is Mrs Hannah Glasse chiefly remembered?
    "First catch your hare."

17. Which writer invented 'Newspeak'? **George Orwell**

18. Is kir a species of Mongolian sheep, an Arabian sweetmeat or a cassis-flavoured drink? **A cassis-flavoured drink**

19. In *Brookside* who succeded David Crosbie as manager of the petrol station? **Cassie Charlton**

20. Who had Muhammad Ali just fought when he said: "It was the closest thing I know of to dying."? **Joe Frazier**

21. Who played the title character in the film *Dr Cyclops*?
    Albert Dekker

22. Is an ablet a fragment of flint, a plant shoot or a freshwater fish? **A freshwater fish**

23. Who had Top Twenty hits with *Searching* and *Stars*?
    China Black

24. Which part of the body is affected by gryposis?
    The nails

25. In which prison in literature was the man who had "killed the thing he loved and so he had to die"? **Reading Gaol**

26. What would you put in a padella: oil, fish or dough?
    Oil

27. In which country was opera singer Joan Hammond born?
    New Zealand

28. In which film, starring Laurence Olivier, did both Alan Bates and Albert Finney make their debuts?
    The Entertainer

29. What would be moored to a ripeck or ryepeck? **A punt**

30. Is a plains-wanderer an Australian bird, an American dust-storm or an Argentinian gypsy? **An Australian bird**

31. True or false: martensite is a form of lacework?
False (It is a form of carbon in iron)

32. What is the collective noun for a group of tigers?
An ambush

33. Who founded RADA? **Sir Herbert Beerbohm Tree**

34. Which was the first British football club to sign a shirt sponsorship deal? **Liverpool**

35. For what is racon an acronym? **A radar beacon**

36. Who had Top Ten hits with *Shazam!*, *Pepe* and *Peter Gunn*? **Duane Eddy and the Rebels**

37. Whose programme on BBC 1 was '*All Talk*'?
Clive Anderson's

38. In mythology, which hero was killed by the blood of the centaur Nessus? **Hercules**

39. From where is train-oil obtained? **Whale blubber**

40. For which fabulous city was Manoa another name?
El Dorado

41. In which constellation is Spica the brightest star? **Virgo**

42. Where are your zygomatic bones? **In your skull**

43. Which sea area lies between Bailey and Shannon?
Rockall

44. Who played Elvis Presley in the 1979 film *Elvis*?
Kurt Russell

45. What was the surname of Jane Austen's *Emma*?

Woodhouse

46. What was Humphrey's role at No 10 Downing Street?

He was the cat

47. In which card game would you score 'one for his nob'?

Cribbage

48. What, in Muslim belief, is the alsirat?

The bridge to Paradise

49. What is the common name for bibliopegy?

Book-binding

50. In which ancient city state were the Ephors the five magistrates? **Sparta**

51. In *Peter Pan* who lived in the dog kennel as a penance?

Mr Darling

52. Complete this Biblical quotation: ''My father has chastised you with whips, but I will chastise you with ...?

Scorpions

53. Who would be guilty of the fraud known as barratry?

A ship's master

54. Who shared the presenting of *The National Lottery Live* with Anthea Turner in its first year? **Gordon Kennedy**

55. What does the Celtic word 'aber' mean?

Mouth of a river

56. For whom did Sir Lucius O'Trigger mistake Mrs Malaprop? **Lydia Languish**

57. Who directed the gruesome 1932 film *Freaks*?

Tod Browning

58. Which word means a distinctive feature, a brief record and a significant sound? **Note**

59. Where did the last confrontation between Red Indians and US troops take place? **Wounded Knee**

60. Whose Top Twenty hits included *Hold On Tight*, *Wild West Hero* and *Evil Woman*? **Electric Light Orchestra**

61. What were or are *ombres chinoises*? **Shadow puppet shows**

62. Beneath which Scottish castle is the Ladies' Rock? **Stirling Castle**

63. Which common surname have Sugar Ray, Edward G and William Heath? **Robinson**

64. True or false: Roger Fry was a painter and art critic? **True**

65. Where was the Minoan civilisation based? **Crete**

66. Which TV series featured characters called Kurt and Ollie Benson, Jambo Bolton and Maddie Parker? *Hollyoaks*

67. In poetry, who was the famous son of Wenohah? **Hiawatha**

68. In which European country is the Grande Dixence dam? **Switzerland**

69. Where did the Germans surrender to Montgomery in 1945? **Lüneberg Heath**

70. At which Test Match did John Arlott give his last radio commentary? **Centenary Test Match (at Lords 1980)**

71. Whose life story was told in the film *I'll Cry Tomorrow*? **Lillian Roth**

72. Who had a No 1 hit in 1957 with *Young Love*? **Tab Hunter**

73. What does a sciophobe fear? **Shadows**

74. Where did Q Fever originate? **Queensland**

75. What sort of a creature is a laspring? **A young salmon**

76. In *Gulliver's Travels* who lived in Glubbdubdrib?
Sorcerers and magicians

77. From which famous book does this line come: "Better to sleep with a sober cannibal than a drunken Christian."?
Moby Dick

78. Which fictional character's parents were played in a TV series by David Horovitch and Polly Adams?
William Brown's

79. In which John Updike novel (and film) did Darryl van Horne appear? *The Witches of Eastwick*

80. Which famous line precedes this one: "And tales of fair Cashmere."? **"I'll sing thee songs of Araby"**

81. Which medical complaint is caused by excess uric acid in the blood? **Gout**

82. Which flower is known as the nuphar?
The (yellow) water lily

83. When was the Open University established? **1969**

84. Which country won all seven titles at the 1981 World Table Tennis Championships (and also had five losing finalists!)? **China**

85. Which poet and lyricist's epitaph was "His foe was folly and his weapon wit."? **W S Gilbert's**

86. To Hindus what are Brahmins, Shatriyas, Vaisyas and Sudras? **The four main castes**

87. What name was given to a person who followed troops and sold provisions, liquor, etc? **Sutler**

88. Who played the title role in the 1936 film *My Man Godfrey*? **William Powell**

89. Apart from a baby-carriage, what else is a pram? **A flat-bottomed barge or boat**

90. What was the name of the 'Portuguese' singer created by Steve Coogan? **Tony Ferrino**

91. Who painted the controversial *Christ In The House Of His Parents*? **John Millais**

92. What colour is cartoon character Marge Simpson's hair? **Blue**

93. Who had Top Ten hits with *When I'm Dead and Gone* and *Malt and Barley Blues*? **McGuinness Flint**

94. What rank was held by G B Shaw's Barbara Undershaft? **Major**

95. What is nanism? **Dwarfishness, being stunted**

96. True or false: Dead Man's Fingers is a fungus? **False (It is a coral)**

97. What is the name for a single dot on a computer screen? **Pixel**

98. To which prison was Edmund Dantes confined in *The Count of Monte Cristo*? **The Chateau d'If**

99. How far in a straight line is it from Land's End to John O'Groats: 603 miles, 628 miles or 642 miles? **603 miles**

100. Who commanded the Luftwaffe during World War II? **Albert Kesselring**

Quiz 22

1. What was Sandie Shaw's second No 1 hit? *Long Live Love*

2. With which sport was Swiss Hugo Koblet associated?
Cycling

3. Who might use the term 'jerkin-head' in his/her work?
An architect

4. Name the actor playing PC Reg Hollis in *The Bill*.
Jeff Stewart

5. Which word means to cool or lessen, a flat-bottomed barge, to turn over and a ship's timber? **Keel**

6. In the film *The Treasure of the Sierra Madre,* two of the three prospectors were played by Humphrey Bogart and Walter Huston: who played the third? **Tim Holt**

7. Whose orchestra was famous for its 'singing strings' sound? **Mantovani's**

8. In Keats' poem who "stood in his shoes /And wonder'd / He wonder'd"? **A naughty boy**

9. To what use was the plant costmary put?
As a flavouring

10. What was a 'First Fleeter'?
One of the original convicts taken to Australia

11. Which London square was nicknamed 'Eisenhower Platz' during World War II? **Grosvenor Square**

12. Who, according to tradition, lent her veil to Jesus to wipe the sweat from his brow on the way to Calvary?
St Veronica

13. Who played the male lead in the film *The Pigeon That Took Rome*? **Charlton Heston**

14. For what is chevrette leather mainly used?
To make gloves

15. Who wear the Sillitoe tartan?
Police officers (round their caps)

16. In Scandinavian mythology, from what did Ymir, the first living being, grow? **Melting frost**

17. In which famous film were Adriana Caselotti, Harry Stockwell, Lucille LaVerne and Roy Atwell heard but not seen? ***Snow White and the Seven Dwarfs***

18. Where were the first Commonwealth Games held? **Hamilton, Canada**

19. Name the character played by Mike Burns in TV's *The Brittas Empire*. **Colin**

20. *The Epic of Gilgamesh* is the Babylonian equivalent of which Bible story? **The Flood**

21. What does a theic indulge in excessively? **Tea-drinking**

22. In which British city is the Robert Gordon University? **Aberdeen**

23. Which river was crossed by the world's first ever cast-iron bridge? **River Severn**

24. Which stretch of land was once called Darien? **The Panama isthmus**

25. Give the name of the character played by Dervla Kirwan in TV's *Ballykissangel*. **Asumpta Fitzgerald**

26. Which team scored 36 all out and 45 all out in a Test Match against Australia? **South Africa**

27. Where did William Hedley and Timothy Hackworth build a smooth-wheeled steam locomotive in 1813? **Wylam Colliery, Northumberland**

28. Which film featured Val Kilmer and Michael Douglas hunting two man-eating lions? ***The Ghost and the Darkness***

29. From what sort of animal does cashmere come? **A goat**

30. True or false: Marks and Spencer were both Hungarian?
False (English and Polish)

31. Who had Top Ten hits with *The Heart of a Teenage Girl*, *A Hundred Pounds of Clay* and *Time*? **Craig Douglas**

32. What is wigan? **A tough fabric**

33. In which country was the medical TV series *Klinik* set?
The Netherlands

34. In which US state is Yosemite National Park? **California**

35. Is an eleme a date, a fig or a plum? **A fig**

36. What does a hyetograph record? **Rainfall**

37. Pigs farrow and dogs whelp: which animals yean?
Sheep and goats

38. Who was the first goalkeeper to captain an England football team? **Frank Swift**

39. In which British city did 18th century architect John Wood achieve lasting fame? **Bath**

40. Perdita, Florizel and Autolycus are characters in which Shakespeare play? ***The Winter's Tale***

41. Which word means serious or sombre, to clean ships and a place of burial? **Grave**

42. In which film did Tom Hanks play Mr White, a record company executive? ***That Thing You Do***

43. Name the actor playing the San Francisco detective Nash Bridges on TV. **Don Johnson**

44. What would be described as 'grand cru'? **Good wine**

45. Where was Captain Cook killed?
Hawaiian (Sandwich) Islands

46. Which archangel foretold the births of John the Baptist and Jesus Christ? **Gabriel**

47. Who wear a yarmulka? **Orthodox Jews (it's a skull-cap)**

48. As what, in later life, did Gertrude Jekyll, painter and embroiderer, achieve fame? **A landscape gardener**

49. Whose Top Ten hits included *Get Down On It, Cherish* and *Ladies Night*? **Kool and the Gang**

50. On which day in 1794 did Admiral Howe defeat the French off Brittany? **June 1st**

51. Before it was identified, what was called 'hospital disease'? **Infection**

52. In which play does Beattie Bryant receive a letter from Ronnie Kahn ending their relationship? ***Roots***

53. Whom was Muhammad Ali fighting in a title fight when he constantly asked: "What's my name?"? **Ernie Terrell**

54. In children's literature which character lived at Puddleby-On-The-Marsh? **Dr Dolittle**

55. What sort of creature is a sea-sleeve? **A cuttlefish**

56. Who played Mr Lawrence in the film *Merry Christmas Mr Lawrence*? **Tom Conti**

57. In a 1996 poll conducted by Classic FM radio who was voted top opera singer of the modern age? **Jussi Björling**

58. Which Labour politician published *The Arms Race* in 1958 and was awarded the Nobel Peace prize in 1959? **P J Noel-Baker**

59. On which sea is the port of Archangel? **White Sea**

60. Which Norse explorer landed in Newfoundland (traditionally) about 1000 AD and named it Vinland? **Leif Ericsson**

61. Who wrote *The Prince and the Pauper*? **Mark Twain**

62. What was the subject of the TV series presented by Frances Bissell? **Food and Cookery**

63. In which film did General Hammond take over Alcatraz and threaten San Francisco? ***The Rock***

64. After the Battle of Bosworth, Henry VII consolidated his claim to the throne by marrying the daughter of which king? **Edward IV**

65. Which member of the weasel family has the Latin name *Gulo gulo*? **Wolverine**

66. True or false: the Colorado Party was active in Uruguay? **True**

67. Who painted *Christ Preaching at Cookham Regatta* and *The Resurrection, Cookham*? **Stanley Spencer**

68. Which book by George Orwell ends: "I shall never again think that all tramps are drunken scoundrels, nor expect a beggar to be grateful when I give him a penny . . . That is a beginning."? ***Down and Out in Paris and London***

69. Who had Top Ten hits with *Dolly*, *My Love*, *Jack In The Box* and *Girls*? **Moments**

70. Whom did Billie Jean King beat in 'The Battle of the Sexes' in 1973? **Bobby Riggs**

71. What is the name of Bart Simpson's father? **Homer Simpson**

72. Where is the Northern Sinfonia based? **Newcastle-upon-Tyne**

73. Is a soleus a block of masonry, a sunspot or a leg muscle?
A leg muscle

74. Who was the first poet to be buried in Westminster Abbey? **Edmund Spenser**

75. Which religion (other than Zoroastrianism) is followed by followers of Zoroaster? **Parseeism**

76. Who presented the TV quiz *Backdate*? **Valerie Singleton**

77. What is blue vitriol? **Copper sulphate**

78. What is measured in steres? **Timber**

79. Which metal is mixed with silver to form sterling silver?
Copper

80. Is a playa a plain, a lake or a volcanic cone? **A lake**

81. Which poet wrote: "Milton! Thou shouldst be living at this hour: /England hath need of thee: she is a fen / Of stagnant waters."? **William Wordsworth**

82. Which French astronomer gave his name to M numbers, used to list star clusters and nebulae? **Charles Messier**

83. Which real-life character was played by Dustin Hoffman in the film *Billy Bathgate*? **Arthur 'Dutch' Schultz**

84. Which Englishman composed the ballets *Pamona, Horoscope* and *Tiresias*? **Constant Lambert**

85. Which was the first instrumental sheet music to sell more than a million copies: *The Entertainer, The Maple Leaf Rag* or *Turkey in the Straw*? **The Maple Leaf Rag**

86. Named after a line of latitude, which channel separates the Andaman and Nicobar Islands?
The Ten Degree Channel

87. Who had No 1 hits with *Such a Night* and *Just Walkin' in the Rain*? **Johnny Ray**

88. Which was the first Communist country to win the Davis Cup? **Czechoslovakia**

89. In which TV series did Michael J Fox play the Deputy Mayor of New York? *Spin City*

90. Who retold the Arthurian legend in *The Once and Future King*? **T H White**

91. What are mined at Coober Pedy in Australia? **Opals**

92. What does an anthophobe fear? **Flowers**

93. Which sea-creatures collect in a smuck? **Jelly-fish**

94. The phrase 'kicking the gong around' occurs in many songs: what does it mean? **Taking drugs**

95. What is another name for ideographs and pictographs? **Pictograms**

96. In films, who has played characters called Wes Block, Jed Cooper, John Wilson and Frank Morris? **Clint Eastwood**

97. What is the common name for electromagnetic radiation in the wavelength range 10^{-11} to 10^{-9}m? **X-Rays**

98. Who wrote the play *The Dock Brief* and the novel *Paradise Postponed*? **John Mortimer**

99. Is Kefallinia a Turkish town, a Greek island or an Icelandic volcano? **A Greek island**

100. Which one word means to cut short, a weed of the genus *Rumex* and a prisoners' enclosure? **Dock**

Quiz 23

1. True or false: Bulgaria joined the Axis in World War II? **True**

2. Which body of water lies between the Peloponnese and the rest of Greece? **Gulf of Corinth**

3. Who played Lady Henrietta Flusky in the original film *Under Capricorn*? **Ingrid Bergman**

4. Who wrote *Brief Diversions, English Journeys* and *English Humour*? **J B Priestley**

5. In which TV series did Dr Marsham and Nurse Carr appear? *Bramwell*

6. Which former pop singer played the owner of an art gallery in the film *Trust Me*? **Adam Ant**

7. What is baked in a saggar? **Pottery**

8. Who was the first man to drive a car at more than 400 mph? **John Cobb**

9. What kind of bird is a pochard: a hawk, a duck or a dove? **A duck**

10. In *Brookside* who ran a shop called *The Gift Box*? **Patricia Farnham**

11. Who had posthumous Top Ten hits with *Brown-Eyed Handsome Man, Bo Diddley* and *Wishing*? **Buddy Holly**

12. Which famous author was Sir Henry Irving's manager? **Bram Stoker**

13. In which film is a small boy called Danny warned by a hotel chef not to go near Room 237? *The Shining*

14. What name was given to the charge levied at hotels on wines consumed by guests but not supplied by the hotel? **Corkage**

15. On the coast of which sea are the ports of Constantia and Sevastopol? **Black Sea**

16. True or false: a woofer accurately reproduces high-frequency signals?

False (It reproduces low-frequency signals)

17. Which one word means sensitive flesh, living and able to learn rapidly?

Quick

18. Name one of the two Football League teams that played a match in 1935 that ended with the score 13-4?

Tranmere or Oldham

19. In which TV series did Sergeant Bilko appear?

The Phil Silvers Show

20. Who had Top Twenty hits with *Take Me To Your Heart Again*, *Roses of Picardy* and *Look Around*?　　**Vince Hill**

21. Who played the female lead in the film *Grease – 2*?

Michelle Pfeiffer

22. Under what name is Temujin better known?

Genghis Khan

23. Who wrote *John Silence*, *The Human Chord* and *Tongues of Fire*?　　**Algernon Blackwood**

24. What exactly competed for the Schneider Trophy?

Seaplanes

25. Which word means potatoes stored in a heap, a fastening frame and a heavy footstep?　　**Clamp**

26. What is the official language of San Marino?　　**Italian**

27. Which was the first non-British country to beat England in England at football?　　**Republic of Ireland**

28. Who slew the dragon Fafner?　　**Siegfried**

29. Which three countries were united by the Treaty of Kalmar in 1397?　　**Denmark, Sweden and Norway**

30. In which TV series were there children called Jason, Erin, Mary-Ellen and Jim-Bob? **The Waltons**

31. Who had Top Ten hits with *From the Underworld* and *I Don't Want Our Loving To Die*? **The Herd**

32. In which David Lynch film did Henry and May have a reptilian 'baby'? **Eraserhead**

33. At universities what name is given to the holder of a chair founded by a sovereign? **Regius Professor**

34. Which capital city was founded on the site where an eagle eating a snake perched on a cactus? **Mexico City**

35. Which county of the Irish Republic begins with 'O'? **Offaly**

36. Which character in *Eastenders* was played by June Brown? **Dot Cotton**

37. Which English poet who died aged 26 left *The Fall of Hyperion* unfinished? **Keats**

38. What is indicated in a mosque by a mihrab? **The direction of Mecca**

39. Is ixia a tropical disease, a nerve ending or a flowering plant? **A flowering plant**

40. Who played Dr Pretorius in the film *The Bride of Frankenstein*? **Ernest Thesiger**

41. Who was loved by Pyramus? **Thisbe**

42. Who was the son of Herod the Great? **Herod Antipas**

43. As what did Sarah Siddons achieve fame? **An actress**

44. What would you find in a psalter? **Psalms**

45. True or false: a wharfinger is the owner of a wharf? **True**

46. Who is the patron saint of Hungary? **St Stephen**

47. What is UTC?
    Co-ordinated Universal Time (Greenwich Mean Time)

48. Who had Top Twenty hits with *I Want That Man* and *French Kissin' In the USA*? **Deborah Harry**

49. Which animals collect in a cete? **Badgers**

50. How many are indicated by the prefix 'tera-'?
    One million million

51. In which country was the Oneida Community founded in 1848: USA, Japan or Brazil? **USA**

52. Which British saint and martyr was put to death with 11,000 virgins by the Huns? **St Ursula**

53. Name the presenter of the TV series *Planet Showbiz.*
    Mark Lamarr

54. With what is silviculture concerned? **Trees**

55. Where in the body is the thalamus? **In the brain**

56. Who became the then youngest ever boxer to win the World Heavyweight Title in 1956? **Floyd Patterson**

57. Of what is gerontology the study? **Old age, aging**

58. Which London edifice used to be called St Stephen's?
    House of Commons

59. Where would you find a riddel, a predella and a ciborium?
    In a church

60. True or false: Oscar Hartzell made a fortune in the 1920s and 1930s selling fake shares in Sir Francis Drake's will?
    True

61. Before David Blunkett who was the last Labour Minister of Education? **Shirley Williams**

62. Which islands lie north west of the Shetlands?

The Faeroes

63. What did the people of Sabden mine in a TV animated series? **Treacle**

64. What is the atomic number of Oxygen? **8**

65. Which helpful gadget was invented by JJ and WR Rawlings? **The rawlplug**

66. Which Irishman was for a long time Frank Muir's opposing captain on TV's *Call My Bluff*?

Patrick Campbell

67. Which word means a betel leaf, a depression in the ground for evaporating brine and to move a camera while filming? **Pan**

68. Who had Top Ten hits with *Love Me* and *If I Can't Have You*? **Yvonne Elliman**

69. Which two actors fought a duel of magic in the fim *The Raven*? **Boris Karloff and Vincent Price**

70. Bernard Farrelly and Phyllis O'Donnell were the first World Amateur champions in which sport? **Surfing**

71. Historically, what is the collective name for Vietnam, Laos and Kampuchea? **Indo-China**

72. Who created characters called J G Reeder, The Squeaker and The Frog? **Edgar Wallace**

73. Ashlar, random rubble, squared uncoursed rubble and rusticated ashlar are all types of what? **Masonry**

74. Who presented the TV series *A Golfer's Travels*?

Peter Alliss

75. How many Articles were adopted by the Church of England in 1571? **39**

76. What do systole and diastole together form?

Pulse, heartbeat

77. Which famous novelist married the Reverend A B Nicholls? **Charlotte Brontë**

78. Is a clingstone a magnetic ore, a lizard or a fruit?

A fruit

79. In which famous film does Marion Crane abscond from Phoenix with $40,000? *Psycho*

80. Who composed *The Carnival of the Animals*?

Saint-Saens

81. Who had Top Ten hits with *The Little Shoemaker*, *Suddenly There's A Valley* and *Alone*? **Petula Clark**

82. Which jockey in 1997 became the third Briton to ride 4,000 winners in flat racing? **Pat Eddery**

83. What is the science of correcting irregularities in the teeth and jaws? **Orthodontics**

84. What did St Columba command to go away in the sixth century? **Loch Ness Monster**

85. Which travel agency shop was run by Alec Gilroy in *Coronation Street*? **Sunliners**

86. William Smith was known as 'The Father of English ...' what: geology, agriculture or archaeology? **Geology**

87. Is tricot a banner, a fabric or a plant? **A fabric**

88. What was Danny DeVito's character name in the films *Romancing the Stone* and *The Jewel of the Nile*? **Ralph**

89. Where were chariot races held in Ancient Rome?

Circus maximus

90. Which ancient Asian people were famous for shooting arrows backwards while riding away from their enemies? **The Parthians**

91. What is placed on the table of the House of Commons when the Speaker is in the chair? **The Mace**

92. Who played the male lead in the film *Marnie*? **Sean Connery**

93. Who had Top Twenty hits with *Tallahassee Lassie, The Urge* and *Palisades Park*? **Freddy Cannon**

94. Which golfer said: "You don't know what pressure is until you play for five bucks with only two in your pocket."? **Lee Trevino**

95. Is a swatch a cloth sample, an insect or a clumsy fellow? **A cloth sample**

96. Where would you find bast, rays and cambium: in a telescope, in a tree trunk or in a cut jewel? **In a tree trunk**

97. True or false: a dabchick is a member of the auk family? **False (It is a member of the grebe family)**

98. Under what name did Edward John Moreton Drax Plunkett write novels, plays, poems, essays and short stories? **Lord Dunsany**

99. Who performed *Love Shine a Light* for the UK in the 1997 Eurovision Song Contest? **Katrina and the Waves**

100. In TV's *Upstairs Downstairs* who was Miss Treadwell? **The Governess**

Quiz 24

1. Where would you usually see caparisons? **On a horse or beast of burden (they are trappings, finery)**

2. Who portrayed Cosmo Smallpiece on TV?   **Les Dawson**

3. With which sport would you associate Martin Kratsev and
    Spencer Oliver?   **Boxing**

4. In which film did detectives Sidney Wang, Sam Diamond,
    the Charlestons and Jessica Marbles appear?
                                            Murder By Death

5. Who had a 1988 No 1 hit with *I Owe You Nothing*?
                                                      Bros

6. Which country won the Olympic rowing eights from 1920
    to 1956?   **USA**

7. Who wrote *The General*, *The Ship* and *The Happy Return*?
                                              C S Forester

8. The Labrador Sea is off the coast of which Canadian
    province?   **Newfoundland**

9. Is icterus a disease, a geographical feature or the beat of
    the pulse?   **A disease**

10. Whose main army was defeated at the Battle of Aughrim
    in 1691?   **James II's**

11. What did L-3 and L-4 do in January 1915?
                    Bombed Britain (They were German airships)

12. Who were the first British group to top the US album
    charts with a debut album?   **Spice Girls**

13. Which Biblical character's name meant 'I have created'?
                                                      Cain

14. What is the common name for nestitherapy?   **Fasting**

15. In which country is the Barkly Tableland?   **Australia**

16. Where was the first book printed in the English tongue (in
    1475)?   **Bruges**

17. Which land in Egypt was given by Pharaoh to the Israelites? **Goshen**

18. Who played Edwina Lionheart in the film *Theatre of Blood*? **Diana Rigg**

19. In which novel does barmaid Rosie Driffield appear? *Cakes and Ale*

20. Tommy Price, Peter Craven and Michael Lee were all World Champions in which sport? **Speedway**

21. What shape is a hippocrepian object? **Horseshoe-shaped**

22. In 1918 Ferdinand I abdicated as king of which European country? **Bulgaria**

23. Which TV series was set in Langton Fields? *Plotlands*

24. Who played police investigator Raymond Avilla in the film *Internal Affairs*? **Andy Garcia**

25. To what did the British and North American Royal Mail Steam Packet Company change its name? **The Cunard Line**

26. What is the mainstay crop of the Indian state of Assam? **Tea**

27. Is a rivière a stream, a huge icicle or a necklace? **A necklace**

28. In which county is the Isle of Athelney? **Somerset**

29. Whose backing group was The Bruisers? **Tommy Bruce**

30. Which sport was involved in the BT Global Challenge? **Yachting**

31. In which body of water is St Helena? **Atlantic Ocean**

32. Stem, straight, satin, fly and lazy daisy are all what? **Stitches**

33. With which song did Bing Crosby, Gracie Fields and Ronnie Hilton all have a Top Ten hit in 1957?

Around the World

34. What was the name of Robert Shaw's character in the film *The Sting*? **Doyle Lonnegan**

35. Which actress appeared in the TV series *Open All Hours*, *Tenko* and *Talking Heads*? **Stephanie Cole**

36. Which king had his right to the Scottish throne secured by the Treaty of Northampton in 1328? **Robert the Bruce**

37. On which river does Antwerp stand? **River Scheldt**

38. Who played Eric Draven in the film *The Crow*?

Brandon Lee

39. Is an aoudad a monkey, a sheep or a camel? **A sheep**

40. Who, in showbusiness, were known as 'Minnie's Boys'?

The Marx Brothers

41. Which football club did Stan Collymore leave in 1997?

Liverpool

42. In which county is Portland Bill? **Dorset**

43. How many pieces does each player have in backgammon?

15

44. Professor Higgins claimed he could pass Eliza Doolittle off as a duchess or even as a – what? – which required better English? **A shop assistant**

45. Which famous poetess was known as 'Ba' by her husband? **Elizabeth Barrett (Browning)**

46. What was the title of the 1986 Football World Cup Grandstand theme by Heads? **Aztec Lightning**

47. Which county was divided into six divisions known as rapes? **Sussex**

48. Which comic-strip hero was created by Stephen Dowling in 1942? **Garth**

49. In which TV town did Sergeant Bonney, PC Rainford and PC Whiteside operate? **Wokenwell**

50. Which pianist began his stage career as Walter Busterkeys? **Liberace**

51. Is a medick a herbalist, a plant or part of a watch? **A plant**

52. With what is Bode's Law concerned? **Distances of planets from the sun**

53. Whose record albums included *Ladies of the Canyon, Clouds* and *Blue*? **Joni Mitchell's**

54. Who played David Crosbie in TV's *Brookside*? **John Burgess**

55. Who played Buddy Holly in the film *The Buddy Holly Story*? **Gary Busey**

56. In which sport would you have a hipe? **Wrestling (It is a throw)**

57. Who was the first actress to allow her name to be used in advertisements? **Lillie Langtry**

58. Who sang with Elton John on the No 1 hit *Don't Let the Sun Go Down On Me*? **George Michael**

59. True or false: there was a Roman emperor called Heliogabalus? **True**

60. What was the nationality of the first non-Briton to win the British Open Golf Championship? **French (1907)**

61. On which river is Newark? **River Trent**

62. For how long did the Biblical flood last? **150 days**

63. What do the Maori words 'kia ora' mean?   **Your health!**

64. Where in Britain was the kingdom of Bernicia?
Northumbria

65. Which film had characters called 2-E, Mr Yunioshi and Paul Varjak?   ***Breakfast At Tiffany's***

66. Which Russian goalkeeper was European Footballer of the Year in 1963?   **Lev Yashin**

67. Who had a 1968 No 1 hit with *Everlasting Love*?
Love Affair

68. For which crime was Robert Hubert erroneously hanged in 1666?   **Starting the Great Fire of London**

69. In which country was the Banner system of military organisation adopted in 1601?   **China**

70. Which US President was nicknamed 'Dutch' until he was in his twenties?   **Ronald Reagan**

71. Which TV animated series featured Magrat Garlik, Granny Weatherwax and Nanny Ogg?   ***Wyrd Sisters***

72. Which world leader had a trial as a pitcher for the Washington Senators?   **Fidel Castro**

73. Was a water-rug a ship's sail, a breed of dog or a beetle?
A breed of dog

74. Who starred in the films *The Frightened City, On the Fiddle* and *Five Days One Summer*?   **Sean Connery**

75. Whose orchestra had Top Twenty hits with *Elephant Tango, Blue Star* and *The Italian Theme*?
Cyril Stapleton's

76. Where would you have found a morsing-hole: on an Aldis lamp, in a braille book or on a gun?   **On a gun**

77. In which sport was Janina Kurkowska seven times World Champion? **Archery**

78. For whom were Kellogg's Corn Flakes originally developed? **Sanatorium patients**

79. Is mullock waste found in cloth factories, gold-less rock or a dish made of shellfish? **Gold-less rock**

80. As what did cartoonist James Gillroy depict the Bank of England in 1797? **The Old Lady of Threadneedle Street**

81. Which Personal Secretary of President Jefferson led an expedition with William Clark to explore west of the Mississippi? **Meriwether Lewis**

82. Which pledge ends: "Pure and holy will I keep my life and art."? **Hippocratic Oath**

83. Which poet wrote *The Land of Heart's Desire* and *The Countess Cathleen*? **W B Yeats**

84. Who was the father of Indira Gandhi? **Jawaharlal Nehru**

85. How many crosspieces are on a papal cross? **Three**

86. Whose Top Twenty hits included *Amateur Hour*, *The Number One Song in Heaven* and *Beat the Clock*? **Sparks**

87. What is similor? **An alloy (Used as imitation gold)**

88. At which Olympics did Helen Wills win two gold medals, Johnny Weissmuller two individual golds and Harold Abrahams win one gold? **1924 (Paris)**

89. Which people used the quipu (knotted string) as a means of calculation? **The Incas**

90. Who wrote *There Is No Yesterday*, *Wind of Desire* and *Harvest of Deceit*? **Mary Faulkner**

91. What is a whisky-jack? **A bird (A jay)**

92. In which film did seven professors study Sugarpuss O'Shea? **Ball of Fire**

93. On TV who presented *The Lying Game*? **Angus Deayton**

94. What was the codename for the Dunkirk evacuation? **Operation Dynamo**

95. Where was the temple in which Samson died? **Gaza**

96. What was the maiden name of the little girl who inspired *Alice's Adventures In Wonderland*? **Liddell**

97. Who wrote *King Rat*, *Tai-Pan* and *Noble House*? **James Clavell**

98. If you had imphee would you eat it, drink it or die? **Eat it (It is sugar cane)**

99. Which is closest to Britain: Dieppe, Le Havre or Rouen? **Dieppe**

100. Who had Top Five hits with *Cool For Cats*, *Up the Junction* and *Labelled With Love*? **Squeeze**

Quiz 25

1. Which comic actor made a record called *My Brother*? **Terry Scott**

2. Who played the title role in the TV series *Captain Butler*? **Craig Charles**

3. How many kinds of orchid are there: 8,000, 11,000 or 18,000? **18,000**

4. Which theory was at the heart of the film *Inherit the Wind*? **Darwin's *Theory of Evolution***

5. Who is the First Lord of the Treasury? **The Prime Minister**

6. Which Indian city has the greatest population?   **Bombay**

7. What does the call-sign letter H (Hotel) represent as a single-letter signal?   **I have a pilot on board**

8. Who was the first batsman to be given out for obstructing the field in a Test match?   **Len Hutton**

9. Who had a 1965 No 1 with *Make It Easy On Yourself*?
    The Walker Brothers

10. Which sovereign state has the shortest length of road?
    The Vatican

11. True or false: a pallet is a hinged cover in an organ?
    True

12. Who wrote *Children of Violence*, *Canopus in Argos*: *Archives* and *The Diary of a Good Neighbour*?
    Doris Lessing

13. Who played Deborah Kerr's husband in the film *Tea and Sympathy*?   **Leif Erickson**

14. Which historical event led Levi Strauss to produce his first denim jeans?   **California Gold Rush**

15. Who painted *Girls on the Bridge* and *Frieze of Life*?
    Edvard Munch

16. Whom did Manuel Santana beat in the 1966 Wimbledon Men's Singles Final?   **Dennis Ralston**

17. Who played the title role in the film *Breaker Morant*?
    Edward Woodward

18. What happens when you haussmannize?
    You reconstruct or improve a town

19. In which city is Sforza Castle, The Ambrosiana, The Brera and the Piazza del Duomo?   **Milan**

20. "Not a drum was heard, not a funeral note, / As his corse to the rampart we hurried.": whose 'corse' was it? **Sir John Moore's**

21. Who was the second cricketer to score 36 runs off an over in first-class cricket? **Ravi Shastri**

22. Which public school did Harry Flashman attend? **Rugby**

23. Mahalpye, Francistown and Serowe are cities in which African country? **Botswana**

24. In TV's *Are You Being Served?* what was the name of Mrs Slocombe's never-seen but often-mentioned friend? **Mrs Axelby**

25. Which insect is sometimes called a twitchbell? **The earwig**

26. True or false: Borough United were the first British non-league club to win a European cup tie? **True (1963)**

27. Who painted *Swan Upping* and *Bellrope Meadow*? **Stanley Spencer**

28. In mythology, how did Minos, king of Crete, die? **He was boiled alive**

29. How many legs do mites have? **8**

30. Complete this consecutive hat-trick of Irish winners of the Eurovision Song Contest: *Why Me?*, *In Your Eyes* and . . .? ***Rock 'n' Roll Kids***

31. Where would you find a fermeture? **On a firearm**

32. Who wrote the play *John, Paul, George, Ringo . . . And Bert*? **Willie Russell**

33. Who played Tarzan in the film in which Bo Derek played Jane? **Miles O'Keefe**

34. In which country is the Lake of the Woods: Canada, Finland or New Zealand? **Canada**

35. One rouble equals 100 what? **Kopecks**

36. Which England test cricketer lost four toes in a boating accident in 1968? **Fred Titmus**

37. Regarding lack of visibility, when does fog become mist? **Between 1 and 2 kilometres**

38. Is byssus a textile fabric, a type of marble or a state of grace? **A textile fabric**

39. What is the popular name for the thyroid cartilage? **Adam's Apple**

40. Which financial aid was introduced in 1659? **Cheques**

41. Which TV series featured characters called Commander Jeffrey Sinclair and Lt Commander Ivanova? ***Babylon 5***

42. What is the common name for an ecchymosis? **A bruise**

43. Which landmark is called Pednanlaaz in the local language? **Land's End**

44. What was a fardier? **An early steam-driven vehicle**

45. Is stephanotis an eye condition, a form of cooking or a tropical plant? **A tropical plant**

46. When did the first Boer War begin? **1880**

47. How many squares are there on a halma board? **256**

48. In the 15th century, which was the traditional month for killing pigs? **December**

49. How did the rag-and-bone dealer, Krook, die in the novel *Bleak House*? **He died of spontaneous combustion**

50. Who captured Havana in 1762? **The British**

51. Who scored the only goal in the 1973 FA Cup Final?
Ian Porterfield

52. Who, after four Oscar nominations, finally won Best Actress Oscar for her performance in the film *I Want To Live*? **Susan Hayward**

53. What is mixed with beer to form the drink 'dog's nose'?
Gin

54. Which of Chaucer's pilgrims played the bagpipes?
The Miller

55. Which was the first feature-length Disney film to be based on original material? ***The Lion King***

56. Who released albums called *Lonely and Blue*, *Cry Softly*, *Lonely One* and *Mystery Girl*? **Roy Orbison**

57. What is cuvée? **(Blended) Wine**

58. True or false: a Quebecker is a native of Quebec? **True**

59. What was Tom Mix before he became a film star?
A US Marshal

60. Agriculturally, what is eddish?
The grass that grows after a mowing

61. Black, white, Jack-by-the-Hedge, treacle, tower and mithridate are all varieties of which plant? **Mustard**

62. What is neutralised by de-gaussing? **Magnetization**

63. Which character in *Macbeth* likened himself to the 'keeper of hell-gate'? **The Porter**

64. Which TV series featured the Hardacre and Fairchild families? ***Brass***

65. In Soling Class yachting, how many crew-members are there? **3**

66. What goes through a sally-hole? **A bell-rope**

67. What kind of garment was a Benjamin? **An overcoat**

68. Bingo, Snorky, Fleagle and Droopy were collectively known on TV as who? **The Banana Splits**

69. Which place-name connects a breed of spaniel, an apple and a Duke's seat? **Blenheim**

70. Who had albums called *Dog Man Star* and *Coming Up*?
Suede

71. In which country did Bing Crosby die? **Spain**

72. If a man was *en grande tenue* what would he be wearing?
Full evening dress

73. For what did Peter Minuit pay about $24 in 1626?
Manhattan Island

74. Which part of the body is the canthus: the angle where the eyelids meet, a muscle in the tongue or the loose skin between fingers? **The angle where the eyelids meet**

75. True or false: a pampero is a wind that blows over the pampas? **True**

76. In the TV series, who took the role of Hetty Wainthropp's husband? **Derek Benfield**

77. What was the first Ford motor car? **The Model A**

78. Where did the Duchess of Hohenberg die in 1914?
Sarajevo (Ferdinand's wife)

79. Where would you find a hardy-hole? **In an anvil**

80. Two Spaniards were the first non-British golfers to compete against the USA in the Ryder Cup. Severiano Ballesteros was one: who was the other?
Antonio Garrido

81. Where did Elizabeth I make a speech to rally her troops in 1588? **Tilbury**

82. True or false: the first World Motor-Racing Championships were held in 1935? **False (1950)**

83. Which part of a coat is also called the revers? **The lapels**

84. Whose albums included *Flaunt It*, *Dress For Excess* and *The First Generation*? **Sigue Sigue Sputnik's**

85. Which word means an animal hide, barren moorland and cruel? **Fell**

86. Is a goaf a simpleton, part of a colliery or a tropical fish? **Part of a colliery**

87. Who played Ivanhoe in the BBC's 1997 TV dramatisation of Scott's novel? **Steven Waddington**

88. What is mixed with whiskey to make Athol Brose? **Honey**

89. Which is the largest lake in the British Isles? **Lough Neagh**

90. What was the name of the Secret Seven's dog? **Scamper**

91. Do cocciferous plants grow on trees, bear berries or have thorns? **Bear berries**

92. When did Tom's midnight garden appear in the story? **After the clock struck 13**

93. In which event did Mary Decker collide with Zola Budd and fall? **3000 metres**

94. For what do the initials JCB stand? **Joseph Cyril Bamford**

95. Who would use a jaw-lever in their work? **Veterinary surgeons or farmers**

96. Whose albums included *The Colour of My Love*, *For You* and *In Conversation*? **Celine Dion's**

97. Who created the detective Piet van Der Valk? **Nicholas Freeling**

98. Which TV comedy series centred around Galfast High School? *Chalk*

99. Where will you find together Copernicus, Pythagoras, Archimedes, Hipparchus and Hercules? **On the Moon**

100. Who, in January 1997, was the footballer sent off after 52 seconds of an FA Cup match? **Ian Culverhouse**

Quiz 26

1. Who played Frank Sinatra's wife in the film *The Man with the Golden Arm*? **Eleanor Parker**

2. To which organisation did Audrey Hepburn devote the last years of her life? **UNICEF**

3. Which county is missing from this Dickensian observation: ''... , sir – everybody knows ... – apples, cherries, hops and women.''? **Kent**

4. During which war were the defensive lines of Torres Vedras employed? **Peninsular War**

5. Because of a receivership wrangle, where did Middlesbrough FC play their first home game in the 1986-87 season? **Hartlepool**

6. Who had albums called *Fear of the Dark*, *A Real Live One* and *A Real Dead One*? **Iron Maiden**

7. In literature, Sydney Carton died because of his love for Charles Darnay's sweetheart: who was she? **Lucie Manette**

8. True or false: *The Tablet* is a weekly newspaper for Jehovah's Witnesses?   **False (It is for Roman Catholics)**

9. Who said: "All I need to make a comedy is a park, a policeman and a pretty girl."?   **Charlie Chaplin**

10. When *Rhapsody In Blue* was first performed, George Gershwin played the piano: which famous orchestra backed him?   **Paul Whiteman and his Orchestra**

11. Which comedian played a drug baron in the TV drama *Supply and Demand*?   **Freddy Starr**

12. Who played Delilah in the film *Samson and Delilah*?   **Hedy Lamarr**

13. Which conductor opposed women players in orchestras on the grounds that if they were pretty they would distract the male players, and if they were ugly they would distract him?   **Sir Thomas Beecham**

14. Which group released albums called *Cloudcuckooland, Sense* and *Jollification*?   **Lightning Seeds**

15. Is hornfels a type of rock, the velvet on deer's antlers or an Alpine musical instrument?   **A type of rock**

16. Who would you find in a casern or caserne?   **Soldiers**

17. Give the name of Charlie and Baz's son in the TV series *Casualty*.   **Louis**

18. Who was the first British monarch to own a Derby winner (Minoru)?   **Edward VII**

19. What is a cep?   **A mushroom**

20. Who appeared in the films *Samson and Delilah*, *The Manchurian Candidate* and *National Velvet*?   **Angela Lansbury**

21. Which astronomer predicted the existence of 'Planet X', the search for which led to the discovery of Pluto? **Percival Lowell**

22. What can be described as chambré? **Wine**

23. What was the famous surname of Lord Redesdale's six daughters? **Mitford**

24. Which English footballer was nicknamed 'The Lion of Vienna'? **Nat Lofthouse**

25. Who was Rutherford Birchard Hayes? **(19th) US President**

26. True or false: according to strict Jewish dietary laws, shellfish are kosher? **False**

27. Is a sand dollar a counterfeit banknote, a sea urchin or a wading bird? **A sea urchin**

28. Who wrote *La Peste*, *La Chute* and *L'Étranger*? **Albert Camus**

29. Who were the invaders in the film *Deadly Invasion*? **Killer bees**

30. Which 1950s star had albums called *Reminiscing, Listen To Me* and *He's the One*? **Buddy Holly**

31. Which Irish abbot founded a monastery on Iona in the Hebrides in 563 AD? **Columba**

32. In which sport was the Lapham Cup the first international trophy? **Squash**

33. Norman Lovett and Hattie Hayridge both played which part in the TV series *Red Dwarf*? **The ship's computer**

34. Who wrote *King Solomon's Ring* and *On Aggression*? **Konrad Lorenz**

35. Which mystic sign was incorporated into the German flag from 1935 to 1945? **Swastika**

36. Justice, Fortitude and Temperance are three of the four Natural (or Cardinal) Virtues: what is the fourth? **Prudence**

37. Which fictional detective was involved in the film *The Gracie Allen Murder Case*? **Philo Vance**

38. Which US novelist wrote *Soldiers' Pay*, *Sartoris*, *As I Lay Dying* and *Light in August*? **William Faulkner**

39. Who hit a golf ball with a six-iron on the moon in 1971? **Alan Shepard**

40. Which US city is known as 'The Big Easy'? **New Orleans**

41. Which island lies directly north of Malta? **Sicily**

42. Who wrote the Gothic novel *Vathek*? **William Beckford**

43. For what does the acronym WASP stand? **White Anglo Saxon Protestant**

44. Is a flying gurnard a knot, a symbol in heraldry or a fish? **A fish**

45. Which former MC5 guitarist had albums called *The Hard Stuff* and *Dangerous Madness*? **Wayne Kramer**

46. Name the actor playing forensic scientist Iain McCallum in the TV series *McCallum*. **John Hannah**

47. What was the subtitle for the film *Star Trek VI*? **The Undiscovered Country**

48. Is a gallinazo a fruit, a lizard or a bird? **A bird**

49. Who succeeded Clement Attlee as leader of the Labour Party? **Hugh Gaitskill**

50. What was Jim Baily the first athlete to do in the US?
Run a sub-four-minute mile

51. Which international organisation was established in Geneva in 1920 to solve international disputes?
The League of Nations

52. Which word connects a breed of dog, a famous expeditionary ship and a channel at the tip of South America? **Beagle**

53. In which TV series did the characters Dr Erica Matthews and Dr Andrew Attwood appear? *Peak Practice*

54. In which sport would you hear the words flèche and conversation? **Fencing**

55. Which term, from Hindu belief, means any person or object considered above criticism? **Sacred cow**

56. Who was the father of James I of England?
Lord Darnley

57. Whose only opera was *Genoveva*? **Robert Schumann's**

58. Traditionally, who was the half-brother of St Jude?
Jesus

59. What name is shared by an island capital, a port in Ontario and a university town in New Zealand?
Hamilton

60. With which club did Jock Stein begin his managerial career? **Dunfermline Athletic**

61. True or false: Field Marshal Kesselring was executed for war crimes? **False (Imprisoned and released in 1952)**

62. Name the actor playing Nick Georgiadis in TV's *London's Burning*. **Andrew Kazamia**

63. Which former Animals' bass guitarist launched Jimi Hendrix and Slade on their careers? **Chas Chandler**

64. Is a caudle a membrane covering a baby's eyes, a wooden spoon or a drink of wine and eggs?

A drink of wine and eggs

65. In Norse mythology, who was father of the Midgard serpent, the Fenrir wolf and Hel, goddess of the dead?

Loki

66. Which religious movement was founded by Charles Taze Russell in the nineteenth century?   **Jehovah's Witnesses**

67. Which famous autobiographer lived in the village of Slad, in Gloucestershire?   **Laurie Lee**

68. Where is the Beardmore Glacier?   **Antarctica**

69. On stringed instruments, what is the chanterelle?

The highest string

70. In 1964, Danny Millman became the first World Champion in which sport?   **Trampolining**

71. Which famous battle was fought near Branxton in Northumberland?   **Flodden**

72. Is a horehound a dog, a plant or a fish?   **A plant**

73. Which bandleader was known as 'The King of Hi-De-Ho'?   **Cab Calloway**

74. Who played John Wayne's wife in the films *Rio Grande*, *McLintock* and *The Quiet Man*?   **Maureen O'Hara**

75. Who became Italy's first Prime Minister after its unification in 1871?   **Count Cavour**

76. Name the presenter of the TV series *Pet Power*.

Anthea Turner

77. Who played Fletch in the film *Fletch Lives*?

Chevy Chase

78. In which concert hall at Snape does the Aldeburgh Festival take place? **The Maltings**

79. Which was the first country to drop bombs from the air? **Austria (1849)**

80. Which group had albums called *Rattus Norvegicus* and *No More Heroes*? **The Stranglers**

81. What is the common name for a decubitus ulcer? **A bedsore**

82. In which field are both the Caldecott and Newberry medals awarded? **Children's literature**

83. In Italian legend who fills children's stockings with gifts on 12th Night? **Befana**

84. Name the host of the TV series *Room 101*. **Nick Hancock**

85. Where is the resort area the Cameron Highlands? **In Malaysia**

86. What "writes; and having writ / Moves on."? **The Moving Finger**

87. Which British writer is the central character of the film *Shadowlands*? **C S Lewis**

88. Was Safford Cape a Canadian promontory, an American conductor or a woollen material? **An American conductor**

89. Which famous poem begins: "Once upon a midnight dreary, while I pondered, weak and weary, / Over many a quaint and curious volume of forgotten lore"? ***The Raven***

90. Who or what would carry out a capriole? **A horse**

91. Which Warwickshire Test cricketer bowled an 18-ball over against Middlesex in 1982? **Gladstone Small**

92. Who was the featured vocalist with the group Union Gap?
Gary Puckett

93. What is obtained by boiling sugar beyond 115°
Centigrade? **Caramel**

94. What do the minor arcana and the major arcana make
when combined? **Tarot cards**

95. Of what are cinnamon, Himalayan, moon, bruang,
silvertip, Tibetan and Andean all species? **Bears**

96. True or false: Margrave was once a German title? **True**

97. Who directed the film *Crimes and Misdemeanours*?
Woody Allen

98. In 1890 William Kemmler became the first person to die
by which method? **Electric chair**

99. Is a sirgang a young elephant, a military commander or a
bird? **A bird**

100. According to legend, who dug the Rio Grande?
Pecos Bill

Quiz 27

1. What kind of vegetable are Kelvedon Wonder, Little
Marvel and Hurst Green Shaft? **Peas**

2. True or false: David Bowie was the first artiste to record
for Virgin? **False (It was Mike Oldfield)**

3. Who played the drunken crop-duster who destroyed the
alien spaceship in the film *Independence Day*?
Randy Quaid

4. Who had a 1987 No 1 hit with *I Knew You Were Waiting*?
Aretha Franklin

5. Who played Drew, the idealistic teacher in the TV series
    Hearts and Minds?   **Christopher Eccleston**

6. Is a motmot a piece of Turkish delight, a verbal *faux pas*
    or a bird?   **A bird**

7. In which sport was Enoch 'Knocker' West a star?
                                                     Football

8. Which burger chain took its name from a Popeye cartoon
    character?   **Wimpy**

9. What was Trevor Howard's profession in the film *Golden
    Salamander*?   **Archaeologist**

10. What is a countermure: a wall, a book-keeper or a
    salesman?   **A wall**

11. What was folk singer and film actor Burl Ives' only Top
    Ten hit?   *A Little Bitty Tear*

12. Name the presenter of the TV show *The Other Half*.
                                                  Dale Winton

13. What was introduced into the Tour de France in 1919:
    drug-testing, the yellow jersey or the King of the
    Mountains?   **The yellow jersey**

14. Is an ogdoad a Gothic arch, a fruit or a series of eight of a
    kind?   **A series of eight of a kind**

15. Who wrote the novels *The Poison Belt*, *The Maracot Deep*
    and *Uncle Bernac*?   **Sir Arthur Conan Doyle**

16. In which musical does Prince Nikki of Murania appear?
                                               King's Rhapsody

17. Where would you have found an ambo?
                                   In a church (It was a pulpit)

18. In which country are the towns of Dordrecht, Sittard and
    Breda?   **The Netherlands**

19. Which word means a rich soup, a stroke allowed to a weaker opponent in golf and a kind of unglazed white porcelain? **Bisque**

20. With whom did navigator Fred Noonan disappear in 1937? **Amelia Earhart**

21. Which mythical Greek fire-breathing monster had a lion's head, a goat's body and a serpent's tail? **Chimera**

22. In which country is the City of Gold coastal resort? **Australia**

23. Whose Top Ten hits included *Tell Her About It*, *We Didn't Start the Fire* and *River of Dreams*? **Billy Joel's**

24. Who played the Pope in the film *Saving Grace*? **Tom Conti**

25. True or false: Cyrano de Bergerac was a real person? **True**

26. Under what collective name did Julius Henry, Leonard, Adolf and Herbert achieve fame? **The Marx Brothers**

27. Who played Brenda in the TV comedy series *Watching*? **Emma Wray**

28. Which fictitious school was attended by Harry Wharton, Hurree Jamset Ram Singh and Vernon-Smith? **Greyfriars**

29. What were Fox, Hendon, Fantome, Barracuda and Gannet all varieties of? **Aircraft**

30. From which creature does the word 'pavilion' take its name? **Butterfly (Papilonem)**

31. Which Irish politician was known as 'the Liberator'? **Daniel O'Connell**

32. Which was the first country to beat England abroad in an international football match? **Spain**

33. Who played a criminal in the films *Dillinger, The Hoodlum* and *Reservoir Dogs*? **Lawrence Tierney**

34. Where on a farm would you find a coulter? **On a plough**

35. Which future Russian leader was expelled from the Tiflis Theological Seminary for 'propagating Marxism'? **Stalin**

36. Who had Top Ten hits with *Love Train* and *Americanos*? **Holly Johnson**

37. Which TV comedy series featured Mrs Stubbs and Mrs Theodopolopoudos? *Birds of a Feather*

38. Is wootz a shoddy woollen cloth, offcuts of rope on a ship or fine quality steel? **Fine quality steel**

39. Which is the first foodstuff mentioned in the song *Food, Glorious Food*? **Cold jelly**

40. What was the original railway gauge used by Brunel on the Great Western Railway? **7 ft**

41. Which sport was played by the Sudanese Manute Bol? **Basketball**

42. Jabirus, jacanas and jacamars are all what? **Birds**

43. Who wrote *Inside Mr Enderby* and *Earthly Powers*? **Anthony Burgess**

44. For what does the acronym TEFL stand? **Teaching of English as Foreign Language**

45. Who allegedly said: "Which of us has not felt in his heart a half-warmed fish?"? **William Spooner**

46. Where would you find the 'Cockpit Country', the Blue Mountains and Black River? **Jamaica**

47. Which British actor played Americans in the films *The Cotton Club, Heart Condition* and *Passed Away*?
Bob Hoskins

48. Name Alan Coren's opposing team captain on TV's *Call My Bluff*.
Sandy Toksvig

49. If you practised maquillage would you be applying make-up, knotting threads or making clay models?
Applying make-up

50. What would you find in a cratch?
Hay, animal feed (It is a manger)

51. What does the German word 'Herrenvolk' mean?
Master race

52. What race was Bruce Hobbs, aged 17, the youngest jockey to win?
Grand National (1938)

53. Who had Top Ten hits with *The Yellow Rose of Texas, Robin Hood* and *Garden of Eden*?
Gary Miller

54. Who painted *Gypsy Girl, Hille Bobbe* and *The Seated Man*?
Frans Hals

55. Of which country is Hvannadalshnukur the highest point?
Iceland

56. What kind of stories did Louis L'Amour write?
Westerns

57. True or false: Anne Frank was Dutch?
False (She was German)

58. Which mathematical techniques, developed by Newton and Leibniz, are based on the concept of infinitely small changes in continuously varying quantities?
Calculus

59. How many No 1 hits did Matt Monro have: 0, 1 or 2?
0

60. Who played scientist Sam Bliss in the TV series *Bliss*?
Simon Shepherd

61. In which film did a rugby team's plane crash in the Andes? **Alive**

62. Which British golfer, when asked for his autograph after two rounds of the 1951 British Open, wrote 'Open Champion' after his name? **Max Faulkner**

63. Who published the novels *Jill* and *A Girl In Winter* and four volumes of poetry? **Philip Larkin**

64. Which motorway has been described as 'a placid, relaxed, under-used road leading to the medieval magic of Winchester'? **M3**

65. Is a tirrivee a wading bird, part of an organ or a temper tantrum? **A temper tantrum**

66. Which element was originally called 'the golden'? **Arsenic**

67. Philip Henslowe's 1592 diary mentions 'Harey Vj': to what was he referring? **Shakespeare's play *Henry VI***

68. What is teff? **A cereal**

69. In which game is ambs-ace the lowest score? **Dice**

70. Which surname connects a Poet Laureate, an English novelist, a US film producer and a Liverpool and England footballer? **Hughes**

71. Which puppets had a Top Ten hit with *Halfway Down the Stairs*? **The Muppets**

72. Is a colibri a flaming torch, a leafy vegetable or a humming-bird? **A humming-bird**

73. Which former British World Middleweight Boxing Champion shot himself in 1966? **Randolph Turpin**

74. Where in the body would you find a basophil? **In the blood**

75. What was the name of the character played by Doug McLure in TV's *The Virginian*? **Trampas**

76. Which newspaper sent Stanley to find Livingstone? ***New York Herald***

77. What sort of creature is a wobbegong: a shark, a marsupial or a wild dog? **A shark**

78. Who played The Khazi of Kalabar in the film *Carry On Up the Khyber*? **Kenneth Williams**

79. Which word means continued progress, a row of bricks and the direction of a stream? **Course**

80. What is the exact word for the ceremony of conferring a knighthood? **Accolade**

81. Which famous love song begins: "I don't need your photograph to keep by my bed: your picture is always in my head."? ***The Very Thought of You***

82. Which of these words did not exist before 1950: microdot, aerosol, biorhythm or doodle? **Biorhythm (1960)**

83. Which country has English as its official language and also uses Pidgin English, Motu and more than 700 local languages? **Papua New Guinea**

84. Which future member of the Royal Family married Lieutenant Earl Winfield Spencer in 1916? **Duchess of Windsor**

85. Who played Peter in TV's *The Piglet Files*? **Nicholas Lyndhurst**

86. In which country are the Churchill Falls? **Canada**

87. In Gabon, what is Fang: a marriage custom, a language or currency? **A language**

88. Who starred in the films *Moon Over Miami*, *I Wake Up Screaming* and *Sweet Rosie O'Grady*? **Betty Grable**

89. Which tennis star was described as "loud, aggressive and . . . personifies a generation which tips its hat to no man."? **Jimmy Connors**

90. Who had Top Twenty hits with *My One Temptation*, *Where Is The Love* and *I Never Felt Like This Before*? **Mica Paris**

91. The Emperor of Ethiopia bought an electric chair but it didn't work: why? **No electricity**

92. What is the collective noun for a group of female seals? **Harem**

93. What was used to buy Aceldama, the burial plot near Jerusalem? **Judas's 30 pieces of silver**

94. What is the capital of Ontario? **Toronto**

95. Which famous family's family home was Renishaw Hall in Derbyshire? **The Sitwells'**

96. What do creophagous creatures eat? **Meat, flesh**

97. Which famous song was orchestrated by Shostakovich and renamed *Tahiti Trot*? **Tea For Two**

98. Who played the lead in the 1989 film *Kickboxer*? **Jean-Claude Van Damme**

99. In which country did the 'Flick bribes scandal' of 1984-86 occur? **West Germany**

100. Who wrote the plays *The Real Inspector Hound*, *Dirty Linen* and *A Walk on the Water*? **Tom Stoppard**

Quiz 28

1. Which film star was selected in 1940 as the possessor of the most nearly perfect male body? **Ronald Reagan**

2.	Who were the first people to mint gold coins, in about 640 BC?	**The Lydians**

3.	Who was the first Spanish woman to win the Wimbledon Ladies' Singles title?	**Conchita Martinez**

4.	Of whom did Charlotte Brontë say: "A little, stout, vivacious lady, very plainly dressed – not much dignity nor pretension about her."?	**Queen Victoria**

5.	Which marine mammal was nicknamed the sea-canary from its whistling?	**(White) whale**

6.	Is sharn a type of rough cloth, cattle dung or a shorn sheep?	**Cattle dung**

7.	Name the subject of the TV series *Blues and Twos*.
	The emergency services

8.	Which scandal resulted from the operation code-named *Gemstone* in 1972?	**Watergate**

9.	H L Mencken coined the word 'ecdysiast' as a more dignified name for which kind of performer?
	Striptease artiste

10.	Fort Duquesne, at the confluence of the Allegheny and Monongahela Rivers, changed its name to what in 1758?
	Pittsburgh

11.	Who played Prince John in the classic 1938 film *The Adventures of Robin Hood*?	**Claude Rains**

12.	Who married Marie Louise, daughter of the Emperor of Austria, in 1810?	**Napoleon**

13.	Where would you find a saddle-spring?	**On a bicycle**

14.	Who wrote the plays *Ivanov*, *The Wood Demon* and *The Seagull*?	**Anton Chekhov**

15.	What connects Steller's Sea Cow, the Tecopa Pupfish and the Stephens Island Wren?	**They are all extinct**

16. Who beat Arsenal with a spectacular last minute goal by Nayim in the 1995 European Cup Winners Cup final?

Real Zaragoza

17. What were the Christian names of Louis and Briggs in the comedy TV series *The Detectives*? **Bob and Dave**

18. Which pop star appeared in the films *Videodrome*, *Hairspray* and *Dead Beat*? **Debbie (Deborah) Harry**

19. What connects Erwin Rommel, Georges Clemenceau and W F Cody? **They all had animal nicknames**

20. True or false: there is a place called Gene Autry in the USA? **True**

21. Which word means the heel of a sword-blade, the cards left in the pack after dealing, the projection on a lock-bolt against which a key presses and the claw of an eagle?

Talon

22. *Gebel-al-Tarik* is now known as which British possession?

Gibraltar

23. Was a trebuchet a trap for small birds, a diamond or a wager? **A trap for small birds**

24. How many times was Ivan Lendl Men's Singles Champion at Wimbledon? **None**

25. What was the name of Superman's mother? **Lara**

26. Who, on TV, was the Hot Chestnut Man?

Johnny Morris

27. Where would you find a pelagic animal? **In the sea**

28. In which US state did the Wright Brothers make their first flight? **North Carolina**

29. Of which fruit are phylloxera the principal pest? **Grapes**

30. "Eileen is married to Jo . . . It is hot in Suez" was the start of the coded message indicating what?

The D Day invasion

31. In which country was the film *Red Sorghum* made and set?

China

32. What would you see in a cenacle?

The Last Supper (or a representation of it)

33. Who composed *Sur l'Herbe*, *Nöel des Jouets*, *Les Bayadères* and *Chansons Madécasses*?

Ravel

34. Who married Charles Hamilton in *Gone with the Wind*?

Scarlett O'Hara

35. Is a garron a chestnut, a horse or a medieval lance?

A horse

36. Which word means a grudge, a copy of a musical work, an account and a notch?

Score

37. Which film director married Ingrid Bergman in 1950?

Roberto Rossellini

38. What is the capital of Tenerife?

Santa Cruz

39. On which Wilkie Collins' novel was the 1940 film *Crimes at the Dark House* based?

The Woman in White

40. Is pombe a drink, a Zulu dance or a lizard?

A drink

41. In 1987, who became the first man to beat Ed Moses in 122 races?

Danny Harris

42. On TV who were Paul Whitehouse and Kathy Burke 'chums' of?

Harry Enfield

43. Which singer was Kirk Douglas's opponent in the film *A Gunfight*?

Johnny Cash

44. What does withershins or widdershins mean?

Anti-clockwise

45. Is a gudgeon a club, a cask or a fish? **A fish**

46. What is the flowery name of the Yellow Poplar or Whitewood Tree? **Tulip Tree**

47. How many countries share the island of Borneo? **3**

48. Which circular dance was named after a US naval hero? **Paul Jones**

49. Whose followers were named 'The 26th of July Movement'? **Fidel Castro's**

50. Which radio serial had its 12,000th episode in 1997? ***The Archers***

51. Jean Lafitte, Anne Bonney, Sandy Gordon and William Thompson were all known as what? **Pirates**

52. The Tucker first appeared on June 19th, 1942: what was it? **A car (4-door sedan)**

53. What is the shape of a falciform object? **Sickle-shaped**

54. Plankton (a form of aquatic organism) drift; what name is given to the aquatic organisms that swim or propel themselves? **Nekton**

55. Which Roman official and writer died of asphyxiation when he ventured too close to the eruption of Vesuvius in 79 AD? **Pliny (the Elder)**

56. Who wrote *Drink With The Devil*? **Jack Higgins**

57. Which Queen of England was called 'the Flanders mare'? **Anne of Cleves**

58. Which cricketer said: "They set me up as an untameable northern savage who ate broken glass and infant batsmen for breakfast."? **Fred Trueman**

59. How tall was Goliath, according to the Bible? **Six cubits and a span**

60. True or false: Henry Ford's first car did not have a reverse gear? **True**

61. In which city was the TV series *Quayside* set? **Newcastle-upon-Tyne**

62. Who discovered sodium? **Humphrey Davy**

63. On which island did Paul Gauguin live from 1891 to 1893? **Tahiti**

64. Which English river's mouth is known as the Hamoaze? **The River Tamar's**

65. Which fictitious hero was orphaned at the age of 11, brought up by his maiden aunt Charmian and went to the University of Geneva? **James Bond**

66. Who painted *Houses On a Hillside*, *The Two Sisters* and *Dancer With Veils*? **Picasso**

67. Craonnese, Mogolicza, Cinta and Casertana are all breeds of which animal? **Pig**

68. Who played Dr Watson to Jeremy Brett's Sherlock Holmes? **Edward Hardwicke**

69. Who was the first driver to win the World Motor-Racing Championship posthumously? **Jochen Rindt**

70. Who was the male lead in the film *The Man in the Gray Flannel Suit*? **Gregory Peck**

71. What would you drink from a copita: brandy, sherry or lager? **Sherry**

72. Name the subject of the TV series presented by Alvin Hall. **Investment/finances**

73. What connects the novels *The Big Sky*, *The Sea of Grass* and *Flint*? **They are all Westerns**

74. Which British gold medallist at the 1960 Olympics did his training in his bathroom? **Don Thompson**

75. Who was US President when British troops burned the White House? **James Madison**

76. Was 'Wild Bill' Hickock buried with his saddle, five playing cards or his rifle? **His rifle**

77. What word is used to describe an improvised piano accompaniment? **Vamp**

78. What did the expression 'to marry Mistress Roper' mean? **To join the Royal Marines**

79. In folklore what were trows or drows? **Dwarfs**

80. True or false: Tom Riley was the Lone Ranger's real name? **False (John Reid)**

81. Who was the 'referee' of the TV programme *Big Break*? **John Virgo**

82. Is tamara a wine, a condiment or a grape? **A condiment**

83. Who were *The Defiant Ones* in the 1958 film of that title? **Tony Curtis and Sidney Poitier**

84. On which sport did the BBC give its first sports commentary (1927)? **Rugby Union**

85. Who married Clementine Hozier in 1908? **Winston Churchill**

86. In which of his plays did Shakespeare mention America? ***The Comedy of Errors***

87. Which letter of the alphabet is called the 'dog's letter'? **R (From its snarling sound)**

88. Bolton and Sayce, H W Goodwin, James Clerk Maxwell and R Fischer were all associated with what? **Photography**

89. Who wrote *To Your Scattered Bodies Go, The Dark Design* and *The Magic Labyrinth*?   **Philip José Farmer**

90. Who was the first cricketer to play in 100 test matches?   **Colin Cowdrey**

91. Which TV game show was presented by Lionel Blair assisted by Maggie Moone?   ***Name That Tune***

92. Which game featured in the Whoopi Goldberg film *Kiss Shot*?   **Pool**

93. Who won Hugo and Nebula sci-fi awards for *The Left Hand of Darkness* and *The Dispossessed*?   **Ursula K Le Guin**

94. Which West Indian test cricketer was the first black governor of the BBC?   **Sir Learie Constantine**

95. Who played Zeus in the film *Clash of the Titans*?   **Laurence Olivier**

96. Where would you find a draught-hook?   **On a gun carriage**

97. Which German boxer beat Jack Sharkey to win the World Heavyweight title?   **Max Schmeling**

98. Who directed and starred in the film *Life Stinks*?   **Mel Brooks**

99. Who rode Sea Swell in the Duke of Gloucester Memorial Trophy race in March 1980?   **Prince Charles**

100. Is ear-cockle a genus of shellfish, a part of the middle ear or a disease of wheat?   **A disease of wheat**

Quiz 29

1. True or false: American Express was the first charge card?   **False (Diner's Club)**

2. J Fred Muggs helped save the *Today* TV show in the US: who was he? **A chimpanzee**

3. What was the name of Alan Shepard's space vehicle? **Freedom 7**

4. Jimmy Greaves played for three clubs in 1961: Chelsea and Spurs were two – which was the third? **Milan**

5. Is traige the refuse in a woollen mill, the refuse of coffee beans or the refuse in a foundry? **The refuse of coffee-beans**

6. Who was the first chairman of the TV programme *Question Time*? **Sir Robin Day**

7. Who wrote *The Tower of London*, *Windsor Castle* and *The Lancashire Witches*? **W Harrison Ainsworth**

8. Which Christian Day is forty days after Easter Day? **Ascension Day**

9. Which part of the body can be described as 'sural'? **The calf of the leg**

10. Is Sandoy Island part of Denmark, Indonesia or Spain? **Denmark**

11. Which Hitchcock film was described by *Time* magazine as "another Hitchcock and bull story"? ***Vertigo***

12. According to James Ussher, Archbishop of Armagh, what was created on October 23rd, 4004 BC? **The World**

13. In which sport did the twins Di and Ros Rowe win world titles? **Table tennis**

14. Name the subject of the TV series *Here's One I Made Earlier*. **Cookery**

15. Which country won the Eurovision Song Contest with *La, La, La*? **Spain**

16. Which famous diet was devised by Dr Herman Tarnower and Samm Baker? **The Scarsdale Medical Diet**

17. Which Canadian province was formerly known as Acadia? **Nova Scotia**

18. Edward Judson, writing as Ned Buntline, gave which famous American a nickname? **W F Cody (Buffalo Bill)**

19. Who played Big John Cannon's brother in TV's *The High Chaparral*? **Cameron Mitchell**

20. Which word means a mixture of clay and water, a dog leash, a small offence and a narrow piece of paper? **Slip**

21. Who provided the voice of the genie in Disney's animated feature *Aladdin*? **Robin Williams**

22. Complete this film septet: Ripley, Kane, Parker, Lambert, Ash, Brett and . . .?
Dallas (Crew of the spaceship in *Alien*)

23. Is a rummer a pedlar, a drinking-glass or a type of shoe?
A drinking-glass

24. Which British actor played Prince Rainier in the film *Grace Kelly*? **Ian McShane**

25. In which country is the Thar Desert? **India**

26. In which TV series did Michael Aldridge and Richard Vernon solve security problems by intellectual means?
The Man in Room 17

27. Field Marshal Montgomery, Virginia Wade and Lord Olivier all had fathers who were what? **Vicars**

28. True or false: Casey Jones died when the Cannonball Express crashed? **True**

29. On which river does Florence stand? **The Arno**

30. On which saint's day did the Battle of Agincourt take place? **St Crispin's Day**

31. Which US President was assassinated in the Temple of Music in Buffalo in 1901? **William McKinley**

32. Is culm a carboniferous rock, a plant tuber or a seaweed? **A carboniferous rock**

33. Which novel by Somerset Maugham was suggested by the life of Paul Gauguin? *The Moon and Sixpence*

34. Whom does a repétiteur train? **Opera singers**

35. How many time zones are there in Europe (excluding Russia)? **3**

36. What name is shared by a Crimean river, a poem by Matthew Pryor and a character in *The Faerie Queene*? **Alma**

37. Which bigger desert is formed by the Kyzyl Kum and Kara Kum deserts? **Turkestan Desert**

38. In mythology, which hunter was turned into a stag and devoured by his own hounds? **Actaeon**

39. Who played the necktie strangler in Hitchcock's *Frenzy*? **Barry Foster**

40. Which famous sports team was originally called the Savoy Five? **Harlem Globetrotters**

41. What are Candomblé, Cao Dai and Chondogyo? **Religions**

42. Who was the first English martyr? **St Alban**

43. Did Yuri Gagarin's surname mean: Hero of the Land, Flying Lightning or Wild Duck? **Wild Duck**

44. Whom did Lizst call "the most poetic of all musicians"? **Franz Schubert**

45. To whom, traditionally, was the Doge of Venice wedded on Ascension Day? **The Adriatic**

46. Is a seckel a pear, an apple or a plum? **A pear**

47. What connects these sporting people: Ian Black, Dorothy Hyman, Ann Jones and David Steele? **They were all BBC Sports Personality of the Year**

48. Who took over from Bruce Forsyth as compère of *Sunday Night At the London Palladium*? **Norman Vaughn**

49. Was a douçaine an ancient medicine, a nurse or a medieval reed instrument? **A medieval reed instrument**

50. What was the name of Ali Baba's brother, who was cut into pieces by the Forty Thieves? **Kassim**

51. Which footballer won his 54th England cap at the age of 42? **Stanley Matthews**

52. Which one word means a group of animals, a tuft of wool, and to assemble? **Flock**

53. What is the opposite of 'euphemism'? **Dysphemism**

54. What is made out of devil's dust? **Cheap, shoddy cloth**

55. Which US state has changed its capital 15 times? **Texas**

56. Who played the chauffeur in the film *Driving Miss Daisy*? **Morgan Freeman**

57. On whose life was Dorothy Baker's novel *Young Man With a Horn* based? **Bix Beiderbecke's**

58. Is a posnet a type of porridge spoon, a bedtime drink or a basin or pot? **A basin or pot**

59. In which European city is the Moorish palace The Alhambra? **Granada**

60. On which instrument was Dennis Brain regarded as a virtuoso? **French Horn**

61. Who played Hoss Cartwright in TV's *Bonanza*? **Dan Blocker**

62. Who designed the Albert Memorial? **Sir Gilbert Scott**

63. Which king of Epirus defeated the Romans in 280 BC and 279 BC? **Pyrrhus**

64. Who was on the cover of the first edition of *Playboy* in 1953? **Marilyn Monroe**

65. For what would you pay multure? **For having grain or ore ground**

66. Who led the Green Mountain Boys in the American War of Independence? **Ethan Allan**

67. What is the capital of the state of New Jersey? **Trenton**

68. Who played Bathsheba in the film *David and Bathsheba*? **Susan Hayward**

69. From which TV series did the TV series *The Power Game* derive? ***The Plane Makers***

70. Which former Police Commissioner advertised Goodyear Tyres on TV? **Sir Robert Mark**

71. In which part of the body is the modiolus? **In the ear**

72. For which US collegiate team did the legendary George Gipp (The Gipper) play football? **Notre Dame**

73. What was the spin-off series from TV's *The Army Game*? ***Bootsie and Snudge***

74. Which famous comic-strip crimefighter was created by Chester Gould? **Dick Tracy**

75. If something was gelastic, would it make you laugh, cry or stretch it?   **Laugh**

76. Who wrote *Vice Versa*, *A Fallen Idol*, *The Talking Horse* and *The Pariah*?   **F Anstey**

77. What was an East Indiaman?   **A ship**

78. True or false: there is an opera called *Punch and Judy*?
True (It is by Birtwistle)

79. In Scandinavian mythology, who were the Aesir?
The gods

80. Where would you find duramen: in finger-nails, trees or igneous rocks?   **In trees (It is the heartwood)**

81. Who, in the 1940s, played the Crime Doctor in a series of ten films?   **Warner Baxter**

82. What did the early Puritans refer to as 'The Whore of Babylon'?   **The Roman Catholic Church**

83. Is a corf a basket, a fastening for the hair or a fortification?   **A basket**

84. Who played the thief paroled to help a government agency in the TV series *It Takes a Thief* ?   **Robert Wagner**

85. Would you find a doublure in a book, on a saddle or under a stove?   **In a book**

86. In which subject was Anders Celsius, proposer of the centigrade thermometer, a professor at Uppsala University?   **Astronomy**

87. Who appeared in the TV series *Goodbye Mr Kent*, *The Norman Conquests* and *Brothers In Law*? **Richard Briers**

88. Which one word means a rule or regulation, a Church decree and a large size of type?   **Canon**

89. What is the chemical formula for carbon monoxide?   **CO**

90. Which team was the first to score from a penalty in an FA Cup Final? **Newcastle United (1910)**

91. Is Wattle Day celebrated in Australia: on June 1st, July 1st or August 1st? **August 1st**

92. Where would you have found the Kroll opera house? **Berlin**

93. Which Shakespeare play has characters called Dull, Costard and Moth? *Love's Labour's Lost*

94. In which European country were the Carpetias a royal house for 450 years? **France**

95. Coombe Hill is the highest point in which range of British hills? **The Chilterns**

96. Which word means the head of a pillar, most important and money used to earn profits? **Capital**

97. George Romney painted many portraits of which famous mistress? **Lady Hamilton**

98. Where would you find a subnivean object? **Under snow**

99. Anything described as pavanazzo has colours like which bird? **Peacock**

100. Which notorious group, founded by Sir Francis Dashwood, met at Medmenham Abbey? **The Hell-Fire Club**

Quiz 30

1. What was the stage name of DJ and chat show presenter Nicholas Henty Dodd? **Simon Dee**

2. Who has been played in films by Angela Lansbury, Helen Hayes and Margaret Rutherford? **Miss Marple**

3.   True or false: there is a fruit called a tangelo?

True (It is a hybrid)

4.   In what does a raff-merchant deal?

Lumber, shoddy goods, etc

5.   Who played the garage-owner in the TV series *Chico and the Man*? **Jack Albertson**

6.   At which sport did Olympic gold medallist Eric Liddell represent his country in 1923? **Rugby Union**

7.   On which Mediterranean island did the Emperors Augustus and Tiberius have villas? **Capri**

8.   Is a Wellingtonia a tree, an orchid or a fish? **A tree**

9.   Which prophetess and witch lived in a cave at Knaresborough? **Mother Shipton**

10. Name the actress daughter of actress Tippi Hedren.

Melanie Griffith

11. Which word means mercy, the divisions of a shield and to provide lodgings? **Quarter**

12. What was a varsovienne? **A dance or the music for it**

13. Who wrote *Signs of the Times*, *Sartor Resartus* and *The French Revolution*? **Thomas Carlyle**

14. What is measured by an eriometer?

Diameters of small fibres

15. Which word means the blade of an oar, the swirling caused by the passing of a vessel and a thin coating of colour? **Wash**

16. If you had a gekkin, would you keep ale in it, play it or wear it? **Play it (It is a Japanese musical instrument)**

17. Which Master of the King's Musick wrote the score for the film *Things To Come*? **Sir Arthur Bliss**

18. Which literary character said: "You might just as well say that 'I see what I eat' is the same as 'I eat what I see' "?

The (Mad) Hatter

19. Which old German coin gave its name to the dollar?

The thaler

20. What does a forester do when he excorticates?

He strips bark off trees

21. Who played the ship's cook who saved the day in the film *Under Siege*?

Steven Seagal

22. Who was the captain of *Fireball XL5*?

Steve Zodiac

23. Who were the first team to win the FA Cup and promotion to Division 1 in the same season?

West Bromwich Albion

24. Who starred in the TV series *Most Wanted*, *The Name of the Game* and *Strike Force*?

Robert Stack

25. In canasta, which cards score the most points?

Red threes

26. Which German word means pleasure in other people's misfortunes?

Schadenfreude

27. Who wrote the music for *Georgia On My Mind*, *Two Sleepy People*, *Heart and Soul* and *In the Cool, Cool, Cool of the Evening*?

Hoagy Carmichael

28. In which city was Enrico Caruso born and did he die?

Naples

29. Of which film actress was it said: "All she had going for her was her talent."?

Bette Davis

30. What does a hatching bird use to break out of its shell?

Its egg-tooth

31. When would a boxer indulge in skiamachy?

When shadow-boxing

32. What are you making if you grind the nib to produce a mass which is then conched? **Chocolate**

33. Which famous dolls were originally drawn in *Woman's Home Companion* in 1909 by Rosie O'Neill? **Kewpie dolls or Kewpies**

34. According to Shakespeare's Sonnet XVIII, what do rough winds shake? **The Darling Buds of May**

35. With which sport was Jim Sullivan associated? **Rugby League**

36. On TV, who played Ironside's coloured assistant? **Don Galloway**

37. Where would you find the red shift? **In the spectrum**

38. Which famous comedy series had episodes called *The Train*, *The Reunion Party*, *The Missing Page* and *The Bowmans*? **Hancock's Half Hour**

39. Which flower's seed vessels provide us with capers? **Nasturtium**

40. True or false: St Peter's in Rome is not a cathedral? **True (It is a basilica)**

41. What is the name of the condition which causes the sufferer to utter obscenities? **Tourette's Syndrome**

42. In which country is the volcano Chimborazo? **Ecuador**

43. Where would you find a macrocyte? **In the blood**

44. Which TV character used to say: "You've all done very well."? **'Young' Mr Grace**

45. Is a nartjie a crocodile, a small orange or a freshwater fish? **A small orange**

46. Who played the priest who tackled the demon in Linda Blair in *The Exorcist*? **Jason Miller**

47. Which title was held by Robert Cecil, Elizabeth I's most able adviser? **Earl of Salisbury**

48. Who wrote *I Know Why The Caged Bird Sings*? **Maya Angelou**

49. By what name is the Roman fortress of Durovernum now known? **Canterbury**

50. Which tennis-champion retired after an accident on a horse called Colonel Merryboy? **Maureen Connolly**

51. To what did *The New English Dictionary On Historical Principles* change its name? **The Oxford English Dictionary (OED)**

52. Who starred in the films *Not As A Stranger*, *The Enemy Below* and *The Sundowners*? **Robert Mitchum**

53. Who composed the operas *Silvano*, *Parisina* and *Lodoletta*? **Pietro Mascagni**

54. What is the predominant colour of wild canaries' plumage? **Green**

55. Who died trying to save Steerforth in *David Copperfield*? **Ham Peggotty**

56. What name was given to the TV programme *The Virginian* in its last series? **The Men From Shiloh**

57. Whose demands were known as the three F's? **The Irish Land League's**

58. During the second half of the 19th century, which country was referred to as 'The Sick Man of Europe'? **Turkey**

59. Which was the first horse to win the King George VI and Queen Elizabeth Stakes in consecutive years? **Dahlia**

60. Is basan or bazan a precious stone, sheepskin used for bookbinding or a religious rite among the Kurds? **Sheepskin used for bookbinding**

61. Which German actor played the lead in the films *The One That Got Away* and *Bachelor of Hearts*?   **Hardy Kruger**

62. Would you find fovilla on Hadrian's Wall, in the teeth or in pollen grains?   **In pollen grains**

63. Is a pekan a nut, a silk gown or an animal?   **An animal**

64. Who played the lead in both series of *Rich Man, Poor Man*?   **Peter Strauss**

65. Which notorious Italian, first names Giovanni Giacomo, died as librarian at the castle of Dux?   **Casanova**

66. Who was the first man to win the World Bowls Championship?   **David Bryant**

67. In *Twelfth Night,* who concocted the plot to make Malvolio wear yellow stockings and smile?   **Maria**

68. Is a goramy a fish, a music teacher or an antelope?   **Fish**

69. What is Sillery?   **Champagne**

70. What would a sufferer from lalopathy have?   **A speech disorder**

71. True or false: cubage is the process of finding the solid contents of any body?   **True**

72. Who played King Arthur in the film *First Knight*?   **Sean Connery**

73. Who wrote *Pantagruel* and *Gargantua*?   **Rabelais**

74. Who would first make a maquette before getting down to serious work?   **A sculptor**

75. What is the chemical symbol of Fermium?   **Fm**

76. Who would be particularly interested in an elf-arrow?   **Archaeologists**

77. Who played Jim Garrison in the film *JFK*?

Kevin Costner

78. Under the Hebrew Law of Levirate, whom did a man have to marry?

His dead brother's widow (if the marriage had been childless)

79. When is a mort sounded on a horn?

On the death of a deer

80. Who wrote *Legends of the Alhambra, Astoria* and *The Conquest of Granada*? **Washington Irving**

81. Which team lost in the finals of the FA and European Cup Winners Cups within four days in 1980? **Arsenal**

82. For whose coronation did Handel compose *Zadok the Priest*? **George II's**

83. Who had Top Ten hits with *The Cutter* and *The Killing Moon*? **Echo and the Bunnymen**

84. What sort of fruit is a mayduke? **A cherry**

85. What was the title of Benedict Allen's TV series in which he travelled along the Namibian coast? *Skeleton Coast*

86. Which film told the story of Vietnam veteran Ron Kovic?
Born on the Fourth of July

87. True or false: lightning never strikes twice in the same place? **False**

88. What is different about the Wave Flower Collection at Harvard University: all specimens are made of glass, none of the specimens is found in the USA or all are orchids?
All specimens are made of glass

89. Which word means duty or obligation, attack, cost and accumulated electricity? **Charge**

90. With which sport would you associate the name Red Grange? **American Football**

91. At which point did Macaulay begin his *History of England*? **James II's accession**

92. The old instrument, the zinke, was the precursor of which modern instrument? **Cornet**

93. Henry Winstanley, John Smeaton and James Douglass all built, at different times, which specific navigational aid? **(An) Eddystone Lighthouse**

94. Which TV comedy series featured characters called Richie Richard and Eddie Hitler? ***Bottom***

95. Which monarch was depicted in the famous engraving by James Gillray entitled *A Voluptuary under the Horrors of Digestion*? **George IV**

96. Off which country's coast is the Gulf of Khambaht? **India**

97. Which spirit is used to make a margarita? **Tequila**

98. Which cartoon team created Tom and Jerry? **William Hanna and Joseph Barbera**

99. Who described Ireland as "The old sow that eats her farrow"? **James Joyce**

100. In which sport did George Mann captain England after World War II? **Cricket**

Quiz 31

1. Which group was founded by a circle of ladies who in 1889 pledged not to wear feathers in their hats? **Royal Society for the Protection of Birds**

2. Who scored Scotland's only goal in the 1986 Football World Cup finals? **Gordon Strachan**

3. Was Thomas Edison's first patented invention the gramophone, a photo-flash or a vote-recording device? **Vote-recording device**

4. Would you find a winze: on a ship, in a mine or under a building? **In a mine (a shaft)**

5. Which one word means a baker's wooden shovel, a fortified tower and rind? **Peel**

6. Who drew the famous 'Careless Talk' posters during World War II? **Fougasse**

7. Which US city is referred to in a song as "you toddlin' town"? **Chicago**

8. Who originally were the worst sufferers of the backache called rachialgia? **Painters**

9. Who composed *Dalibor* and *The Kiss*? **Smetana**

10. Who was allegedly put to death 'in a butt of Malmsley' in the Tower of London in 1478? **Duke of Clarence**

11. Who had a 1958 No 1 hit with *Hoots Mon*? **Lord Rockingham's XI**

12. Which Disney cartoon film was remade as a live-action film starring Martin Landau in 1996? *Pinocchio*

13. Who played Inspector Jordan in TV's *Special Branch*? **Derren Nesbitt**

14. Which planet has moons called Fear and Terror? **Mars**

15. What, in computing, is CAD? **Computer-aided design**

16. Which boxer won the WBC light-heavyweight and super middleweight titles in 1988 after a 19 month lay-off? **Sugar Ray Leonard**

17. In the E W Hornung stories what eventually happened to Raffles? **He was killed in the Boer War**

18. Whom did Estella marry in *Great Expectations*? **Bentley Drummle**

19. Is a manakin a small man, a bird or a religious utensil? **A bird**

20. Which surname was shared by an American jazz saxophonist, an English Egyptologist and a US President? **Carter**

21. Who wrote the orchestral works *Bells Across the Meadows* and *Sanctuary of the Heart*? **Albert Ketèlby**

22. Who had Top Twenty hits with *Grandpa's Party*, *It's a Shame* and *Born 2 B R E E D*? **Monie Love**

23. What does CPAG stand for? **Child Poverty Action Group**

24. Who was Minister of Overseas Development 1964-65, Minister of Transport 1965-66, Secretary of State for Employment and Productivity 1968-70 and Minister of Health and Social Security in 1968? **Barbara Castle**

25. Who had left the infant Jack Worthing in a handbag at a station before *The Importance of Being Ernest* begins? **Miss Prism**

26. Who played the knight Bowen in the film *Dragonheart*? **Dennis Quaid**

27. What is the next line in this poem: ''The common cormorant or shag . . .''? **Lays eggs inside a paper bag**

28. Before his untimely death Labour Leader John Smith had achieved 108 out of 227 what? **Munros (mountains)**

29. Who on radio was 'The Memory Man'? **Leslie Welch**

30. In the 15th-17th centuries what sort of person was a lansquenet? **A mercenary soldier**

31. Which novel by Sir Walter Scott is also known as *The Cavalier*? **Woodstock**

32. Which Welsh actor played the title role in TV's *Stryker of Scotland Yard*? **Clifford Evans**

33. In how many balls did Tom Moody of Warwickshire score a century against Glamorgan in 1990: 36 balls, 43 balls or 47 balls? **36 balls**

34. True or false: himation is another word for hibernation? **False (It is a Greek garment)**

35. Who married Percy Sugden's niece in TV's *Coronation Street*? **Bill Webster**

36. What is known as 'universal arithmetic'? **Algebra**

37. What was Madness's only No 1 hit? *House of Fun*

38. From which sea creature does tomalley come? **Lobster**

39. Is skilly a servant's pay, a shepherd's code of whistles or a thin broth? **A thin broth**

40. What title is given to a Bishop who assists the Bishop of a diocese? **Bishop Suffragan**

41. Which capital city was the setting for the film *Nothing Personal*? **Belfast**

42. Which unit of length was once defined as the distance between two gold plugs on a bronze bar? **The yard**

43. Who had Top Twenty hits with *Hole Hearted*, *Song For Love* and *Tragic Comic*? **Extreme**

44. In what sphere might a contango be paid? **Stock Exchange transactions**

45. Which TV series had characters called Tarot, Lulli and Sam and an owl called Ozymandias? **Ace of Wands**

46. Who would use a banderilla in his work? **A bull-fighter**

47. Who was the first man to travel at more than 300mph on land? **Malcolm Campbell**

48. What are Doppers, Dunkers, Dukhobors and Tunkers? **Members of religious sects**

49. Would you find a bitt in a carpenter's shop, on a ship or above a barn? **On a ship (Post)**

50. Which country did Napoleon defeat at the Battle of Wagram? **Austria**

51. True or false: Angela Mortimer won only one Grand Slam singles title? **False (She won three)**

52. What undergoes the Carnot cycle? **Gas (in a heat engine)**

53. What is the state capital of South Carolina? **Columbia**

54. Which US writer and civil rights activist said: "Anyone who has ever struggled with poverty knows how extremely expensive it is to be poor."? **James Baldwin**

55. In which dance would a caller have shouted "Shine", "Peel" and "Cut the Core"? **The Big Apple**

56. Who played Dracula in the 1996 film *Dracula: Dead and Loving*? **Leslie Nielsen**

57. Who had Top Twenty hits with *Don't Stay Away Too Long*, *Rainbow* and *Hey Mr Music Man*? **Peters and Lee**

58. Who played Arthur in the TV series *Arthur of the Britons*? **Oliver Tobias**

59. Which Welsh singer was billed as "Radio's Cavalier of Song"? **Donald Peers**

60. What was the nickname of England test cricketer George Oswald Browning Allen? **Gubby**

61. Which popular comic actor published the books *Boudoir of Bathing Beauties* and *Ooh-la-la!*? **Ronnie Barker**

62. Which ornamentative movement took its name from the French for rock or shell? **Rococo**

63. Who led an uprising against Henry VI in 1450? **Jack Cade**

64. Who was the first ragtime composer to write down his music? **Scott Joplin**

65. Who regularly opened his comedy routines with the words "The day war broke out . . ."? **Robb Wilton**

66. Into which religion was the religion Bon absorbed? **Tibetan Buddhism**

67. Which toy does Arnold Schwarzenegger try to get his son in the film *Jingle All the Way*? **Turbo-Man**

68. In *Othello* who is the husband of Emilia? **Iago**

69. Which screen cowboy had a dog called Bullet? **Roy Rogers**

70. Who had Top Three hits with *3 AM Eternal, Last Train To Trancentral* and *Justified and Ancient*? **KLF**

71. In which archipelago is Tahiti? **Society Islands**

72. On which golf course would you see the Swilcan Bridge? **St Andrew's**

73. Which drink was advertised with the slogan: "Open, Pour, Be Yourself Once More"? **Oasis**

74. From what is the paste, tahini, made? **Sesame seeds**

75. On which circuit did World Motor-Racing Champion Jim Clark die? **Hockenheim**

76. Which future saint took part in the stoning of St Stephen? **St Paul**

77. Which organisation has its HQ at Weltpoststrasse 4 in Berne? **Universal Postal Union**

78. What was Miss Piggy's character name in *Muppet Treasure Island*? **Benjamina Gunn**

79. In the Republic of Ireland, what is the Tánaiste? **Deputy Prime Minister**

80. What was the name of Patrick Newell's character in the TV series *The Avengers*? **Mother**

81. Who became Chairman of the Conservative party after the 1997 General Election? **Cecil Parkinson**

82. Which Black Sea port was the site of an Allied Conference in 1945? **Yalta**

83. Who had Top Twenty hits with *D W Washburn*, *Valleri* and *Alternate Title*? **The Monkees**

84. Was a pullicat a handkerchief, a string tie or a glove? **A handkerchief**

85. Which was the only club to win the FA Cup in successive seasons in the 1970s? **Tottenham Hotspur**

86. What are carrageen, sea lettuce and tangle? **Seaweeds**

87. What colour jersey is worn by the King of the Mountains in the Milk Race? **Red**

88. Which word means part of a loom, the stem of certain marsh plants and a strip of metal or wood inserted into a wind instrument? **Reed**

89. In the Old Testament who was the son of Lamech?

Noah

90. Who played Rocky Cassidy in the TV series *Boon*?

Neil Morissey

91. What is the other name for Green Monkey disease?

Marburg disease

92. In which film does Joanna Lumley play Aunt Spiker and Miriam Margoyles play Aunt Sponge?

James and the Giant Peach

93. True or false: Royal swans have two nicks on their bills?

False (They are unmarked)

94. Who wrote *North and South* and *Cranford*?

Elizabeth Gaskell

95. Which river runs through Bratislava?   **The Danube**

96. Is a girasol a flightless bird, a variety of opal or a spinning-top?   **Variety of opal**

97. Under what name did Camille Javal achieve international film stardom?   **Brigitte Bardot**

98. In which country are the cities of Ålborg, Århus and Randers?   **Denmark**

99. Where is Lord Horatio Nelson buried?

St Paul's Cathedral

100. Was a rebec a sailing ship, a torture device or musical instrument?   **Musical instrument**

Quiz 32

1. Which boy was the companion of the strange cartoon creature, Flook?   **Rufus**

2. Which insect gets its scientific name from the Latin for 'little scissors'? **Earwig (Forficula)**

3. Who wrote *Black Narcissus*, *In This House Of Brede* and *The Dark Horse*? **Rumer Godden**

4. In *Coronation Street,* give Sean Skinner's occupation. **Bookmaker**

5. According to the Mock Turtle, of what were Ambition, Distraction, Uglification and Derision branches? **Arithmetic**

6. What was the original name of The Old Vic theatre? *Royal Coburg*

7. Who is the wife of Babar, King of the Elephants? **Celeste**

8. In a film, what was unusual about Mr Drake's duck? **It laid uranium eggs**

9. Which musical instrument was called the fagotto? **The bassoon**

10. Old Joe, from Barnum and Bailey's circus, was the model for the original what? **Camel on *Camel* cigarettes**

11. Who became the youngest ever Grand Slam Singles winner by winning the Australian Women's Singles in January 1997? **Martina Hingis**

12. On which island do the Dyaks live? **Borneo**

13. To what is there a momument in Guachala in Ecuador? **The Equator**

14. Give the name of Gordon Muir's son in TV's *Holding the Baby*. **Daniel**

15. In which Dickens' novel does John Harmon assume the identity of John Rokesmith, and fall in love with Bella Wilfer? **Our Mutual Friend**

16. What did Colonel Pierpoint have installed in St James's Street in 1864? **The first traffic island**

17. Whose Top Ten hits included *Johnny Will*, *Sugar Moon* and *It's Too Soon To Know*? **Pat Boone**

18. Who managed Arsenal when they did the double in 1971? **Bertie Mee**

19. What is Florida water?
A perfume (like Eau de Cologne)

20. In films which group went on *The Next Mission*, *The Deadly Mission* and *The Fatal Mission*?
The Dirty Dozen

21. Which writer and essayist, himself mentally unstable, cared for his insane sister, Mary, who co-wrote with him?
Charles Lamb

22. True or false: potlatch was a Red Indian custom of giving gifts? **True**

23. Give the nationality of the singer Céline Dion. **Canadian**

24. What do we call the record of the Great Inquest of 1086?
Domesday Book

25. Which secret society took its name from the Greek for 'circle'? **Ku Klux Klan**

26. What is the adjective from 'deacon'? **Diaconal**

27. What were shawms, bombards and pommers?
Musical instruments

28. Is genevrette a cotton textile, a type of pocket-watch or a wine? **A wine**

29. From which club did Liverpool sign Kevin Keegan?

Scunthorpe Utd

30. Who built *The Rocket,* the early locomotive?

Robert Stephenson

31. Which Canadian territory forms most of Alaska's border?

Yukon

32. For whom did Douglas Bader work before and after World War II? **Shell Oil**

33. Name the host of the TV word programme *The Alphabet Game*. **Andrew O'Connor**

34. Lancaster House stands in the precincts of which royal building? **St James's Palace**

35. Is a rough-hound a fish, a mongrel dog or a metal plate?

A fish

36. What was the second No 1 hit for the Spencer Davis Group? *Somebody Help Me*

37. What is a tarantass? **A four-wheeled carriage**

38. What was the name of the Knight of the Leopard in *The Talisman*? **Sir Kenneth**

39. Which film character, played by Johnny Weissmuller, was described as 'Tarzan with clothes on'? **Jungle Jim**

40. The islands of Wellington, Hanover and Londonderry are part of which country? **Chile**

41. In which sport would you win the Stewards Cup and the Silver Goblets? **Rowing**

42. Where did Charles I raise his standard at the start of the English Civil War? **Nottingham**

43. In the early days of the cinema, what were 'inkies'?

Incandescent lights

44. Where do the cartoon family The Simpsons live?
Springfield

45. Which insect transmits sleeping sickness? **Tsetse Fly**

46. Who wrote the plays *Thark*, *Plunder* and *Rookery Nook*?
Ben Travers

47. In the film *Geordie*, at which event did Geordie win an Olympic gold medal? **Throwing the hammer**

48. What were written by Temple Fielding, Ed Buryn, Robert Kane and Bradley Smith? **Travel guidebooks**

49. What was the popular name for the De Havilland 121 3-engined jet, introduced in 1964? **Trident**

50. Who had Top Ten hits with *My Brother Jake* and *Wishing Well*? **Free**

51. What is a Mari Lwyd? **A hobby horse**

52. Who was the first boxer to defeat Chris Eubank professionally? **Steve Collins**

53. On which river does Ely stand? **River Ouse**

54. Which actress fell overboard in the 1987 film *Overboard*?
Goldie Hawn

55. Would you play, eat or squash a chittarone?
Play it (It is a lute)

56. Who is the Duke of Lancaster? **The Queen**

57. Which country's territory increased by 100,000 square miles after an earthquake in 1822? **Chile**

58. Which word means to come down, a lamp, a window and frivolous? **Light**

59. In the Bible, what was Lake Tiberias? **Sea of Galilee**

60. Name the host of the TV quiz show *Goldmaster*.

Mike Read

61. What kind of sport is langlauf?   **Cross-country skiing**

62. Which Wimbledon tennis champion's name meant 'Tall trees by still water'?   **Evonne Goolagong**

63. True or false: Rebecca Stephens was the first British woman to climb Mount Everest?   **True**

64. In mythology, what were Tiphys, Hercules, Hylas, Orpheus, Castor, Pollux and 44 others called?

The Argonauts

65. In films what was Mad Max's surname?   **Rockatansky**

66. With which group do you associate Damon Albarn?

Blur

67. Which dog breed is known as the Old English terrier?

The Airedale terrier

68. The NRA grades water in five classes: 1A, 2, 3 and 4 are four of the classes – what is the fifth?   **1B**

69. What sort of garment is a calotte?

A skull-cap (It is worn by priests)

70. What was the original name of the liner *Norway,* launched in 1979?   *France*

71. With which sport was Fulke Walwyn associated?

Horse-racing

72. Is a fent an opening in a garment, an underground volcanic chamber or a plant shoot?

An opening in a garment

73. To whom did Mr Charrington rent a room above his shop in *1984*?   **Winston and Julia**

74. Carinthia and Thuringia were parts of which country in the 10th century? **Germany**

75. When the midweek lottery draw began in February 1997, who presented it? **Carol Smillie**

76. According to Thomas Hobbes, what was man's natural state? **War**

77. What kind of window, with a sharply pointing arch, is named after a surgical instrument? **Lancet**

78. In Anglo-Saxon England, what was a gemote?
A court or meeting

79. Who co-starred with Billy Crystal in the film *Forget Paris*? **Debra Winger**

80. As what was Humphrey Repton famous in the 18th and 19th centuries? **Landscape gardener**

81. How did lineswoman Dorothy Cavis-Brown make the news at Wimbledon in 1964? **She fell asleep**

82. The UN has six official languages: English, French, Chinese, Spanish and Russian are five – what is the sixth?
Arabic

83. Who was the last man to win the Wimbledon Men's Singles as an amateur? **John Newcombe**

84. What sort of animal is a gib? **A cat**

85. In the story *Babbitt*, where did George Babbitt live?
Zenith City

86. Who succeeded Tommy Docherty as Scotland manager in 1973? **Willie Ormond**

87. Whom did Kristine Kochanski replace in the TV series *Red Dwarf*? **Rimmer**

88. When Sylvester Stallone was Ray Tango, who was Gabe Cash? **Kurt Russell**

89. Which dinosaur's name meant 'three-horned'? **Triceratops**

90. What, in Central Asia, is a yurt? **A tent**

91. Is a bourrée a thick soup, a priest's stole or a dance? **A dance**

92. Who played Carlito Brigante in the film *Carlito's Way*? **Al Pacino**

93. Who defeated Henry III at Lewes, but was killed at the Battle of Evesham in 1265? **Simon de Montfort**

94. Who said: "This generation of Americans has a rendezvous with destiny."? **F D Roosevelt**

95. Which football team is nicknamed The Saddlers? **Walsall**

96. The Alexander Archipelago is part of which country? **USA**

97. Where are Koplik's spots found? **Behind the back teeth [Accept in the mouth.]**

98. In which famous poem do the knights of Justice, Courtesy, Temperance and Holiness appear? ***The Faerie Queene***

99. Who, in 1968, made what was known as 'the jump into the 21st century'? **Bob Beamon**

100. Give the name of Sinbad's daughter in TV's *Brookside*. **Ruth**

Quiz 33

1. Which British island is called Ynys Mon? **Anglesey**

2.	Which TV game show about antiques was chaired by Michael Parkinson?		***Going For a Song***

3.	True or false: there is a Kangaroo Island in Australia?

	True

4.	Who played the lead and directed the film *Home At Seven*?		**Ralph Richardson**

5.	Which code was devised by Depillon, was modified by Popham and improved by Charles Pasley?		**Semaphore**

6.	What was Robert Picardo's position on Star Trek's *Voyager*?		**Doctor**

7.	What is a lauwine?		**An avalanche**

8.	At certain times which creatures form the biggest concentration of large animals on earth?

	Wildebeeste (Gnu)

9.	Which football club had four managers in 1981?

	Queen's Park Rangers

10.	Of what is brachylogy the study: concise speech, coral or the size of skulls?		**Concise speech**

11.	Saginaw Bay, Bruce Peninsula and Great Duck Island are all in which lake?		**Lake Huron**

12.	Name the host of the TV series *Fortean TV*.

	Lionel Fanthorpe

13.	Who wrote *The White Devil*?		**John Webster**

14.	Is a palberry a horse, a currant or a cross between a bilberry and an elderberry?		**Currant**

15.	Which event was won by Ludger Beerbaum in the 1992 Olympics?		**Show-jumping**

16.	On which marking would you see the letters TF, F, T, S, W and WNA?		**Plimsoll Line**

17. What was the devil called in *The Devil and Daniel Webster*? **Mr Scratch**

18. Papelitos were the forerunners of which common objects? **Cigarettes**

19. Is a wishtonwish a wind, a prairie-dog or a flowering shrub? **Prairie-dog**

20. What was the main setting for the film *Dawn of the Dead*? **A shopping-mall**

21. Which Asiatic city was originally founded as Dagon? **Rangoon**

22. What colour are hot (Type 0) stars? **Blue**

23. Which was the first football team to advance from the Third Division to the First Division in consecutive seasons? **Charlton Athletic**

24. What do the Queens hold in a pack of cards? **A flower**

25. Is a collection of woodpeckers a knot, a descent or a roost? **A descent**

26. Who played Anna Fairley in the TV series *Reckless*? **Francesca Annis**

27. Which Shakespearean character was described as ''the triple pillar of the world, transformed into a strumpet's fool''? **Mark Antony**

28. What name is given to the technique of laying on paint so thickly that it protrudes from the surface of the canvas? **Impasto**

29. Who played the title role in the 1996 film *Michael Collins*? **Liam Neeson**

30. Of which Sunderland and Derby County footballer was it said: ''He carries space around with him like an umbrella.''? **Raich Carter**

31. Which Prime Minister's actual name was Robert Arthur Talbot Gascoyne-Cecil? **Marquess of Salisbury**

32. Who took command of the circumnavigation voyage after Magellan was killed? **El Cano**

33. What did the Combination Laws of 1799 and 1800 make illegal? **Trade Unionism**

34. What does the Spanish word 'galapago' mean? **Tortoise**

35. Which *ITMA* character said: "I don't mind if I do"?
Colonel Chinstrap

36. Which character in TV's *Dad's Army* was played by Colin Bean? **Private Sponge**

37. Who wrote *Way of an Eagle*, *The Keeper of the Door* and *Storm Drift*? **Ethel M Dell**

38. Which country was expelled from the Organisation of American States in 1962? **Cuba**

39. Is braxy a prickly shrub, stagnant water or a disease of sheep? **A disease of sheep**

40. In which country is Ninety Mile Beach? **Australia**

41. In which story are the sunbathing Helen and Anthony disturbed when a dog falls from an aeroplane?
Eyeless in Gaza

42. Which island was the location for the film *To Have and Have Not*? **Martinique**

43. Which breed of dog is also called the Gazelle Hound?
The Saluki

44. What can be described as 'pétillant'?
Wine (Slightly sparkling)

45. True or false: Neptune is larger than Uranus? **False**

46. Who wrote the poems *The Forsaken Merman*, *The Scholar Gypsy* and *Sohrab and Rustum*?   **Matthew Arnold**

47. Who presented a TV talk show called *Funky Bunker*?
                                              Craig Charles

48. What was bowler R P Baker's batting average in the 1977 cricket season: 0, 1 or 102?   **102**

49. Which African country is closest to Italy?   **Tunisia**

50. What does a cruiskeen hold?   **Spirit, whiskey, liquor**

51. Who wrote *Mrs Dalloway* and *The Voyage Out*?
                                              Virginia Woolf

52. Which couple won Britain's only gold medal at the 1952 Olympics?   **Harry Llewellyn and *Foxhunter***

53. In which TV series did Howard Jacobson look at comedy and its implications?   ***Seriously Funny***

54. What is the state capital of Oregon?   **Salem**

55. Sialorrhea is an excess of what?   **Saliva**

56. Who co-starred as Richard Dreyfus' partner in the films *Stakeout* and *Another Stakeout*?   **Emilio Estevez**

57. Which word means loose rock, slight indisposition caused by a disorder of the alimentary canal and impertinent?
                                              Brash

58. True or false: a sumpit is a poisoned arrow?   **True**

59. Off which country's coast is the Gulf of Martaban?
                                              Myanmar (Burma)

60. Who is the wizard in *The Hobbit* and *The Lord of the Rings*?   **Gandalf**

61. Of which sport is rejoneo a form?   **Bullfighting**

62. Which TV series was presented by Antoine de Caunes and Jean-Paul Gaultier? **_Eurotrash_**

63. What was achieved by Bert Turner (1946) and Tommy Hutchison (1981) in FA Cup Finals?
Scored for both sides

64. Which king in a pack of cards does not have a moustache? **King of Hearts**

65. True or false: Port Said is on the Red Sea?
False (Mediterranean)

66. Which entertainer was born Cherilyn La Pier? **Cher**

67. Who is the patron saint of needlewomen and laundry workers? **St Clare**

68. Which famous book was originally written in Kuffic?
The _Koran_

69. Who played Solomon in the film _Solomon and Sheba_?
Yul Brynner

70. Which illness was formerly known as grippe? **Influenza**

71. Around 1750 AD, which was the world's largest city?
Tokyo

72. Which was the only Eastern bloc country to compete in the 1984 Olympics? **Romania**

73. Who, in _Treasure Island,_ was pinned to the mast by a knife? **Jim Hawkins**

74. Which scientist said: "If only I had known, I should have become a watchmaker."? **Einstein**

75. What did Talleyrand refer to as "the beginning of the end" in 1812? **Napoleon's retreat from Moscow**

76. What were first described by Antipater of Sidon in the 2nd century BC? **The Seven Wonders of the World**

77. Who played Doc Holliday in the 1993 film *Tombstone*?

Val Kilmer

78. Who asked the questions in the 1997 TV series *Face To Face*?

Jeremy Isaacs

79. Is a quinella a long cloak, a leaf with five points or a type of bet?

A type of bet

80. What name was given to the ships used as prisons in Britain in the 18th and 19th centuries?

Hulks

81. What was odd about Saki's character Gabriel-Ernest?

He was a lycanthrope (thought he was a wolf)

82. Which is the only one of the Great Lakes wholly in the USA?

Lake Michigan

83. What colour is a porraceous object?

Green

84. What sort of creature is a quarl: a bird, a jelly-fish or a monkey?

A jelly-fish

85. Which one word means beer or ale spiced with wormwood, a gentle bubbling sound, a heavy fall and an inverted stitch in knitting?

Purl

86. Who rode the Derby winners Grady, Golden Fleece and Quest For Fame?

Pat Eddery

87. Who presented a TV series called *Paradise Gardens*?

Geoff Hamilton

88. Which literary schoolboy had the Christian names John Christopher Timothy?

Jennings

89. In which sport was Dick Button Olympic and World Champion?

Figure skating

90. Who played Gomez Addams in the film *The Addams Family Values*?

Raul Julia

91. Was a regular Atlantic steamship service inaugurated in 1838, 1848 or 1858? **1838**

92. What connects El Galeras, Erebus, Semeru and Guallatiri? **They are volcanoes**

93. What fond name is often given to the 55 delegates who drafted the US Constitution? **Founding Fathers**

94. True or false: George Washington was aide-de-camp to General Braddock in the British army? **True**

95. Who separated Coe and Ovett at the finish of the 1980 Olympics 1500 metres? **Jurgen Straub**

96. In which TV series was there a pig called Arnold Ziffel? ***Green Acres***

97. In which Shakespeare play does Friar Lawrence play an important part? ***Romeo and Juliet***

98. Which region of England suffered an earthquake measuring 3.5 on the Richter scale in 1994? **East Anglia**

99. Which famous story is told from a different angle in the film *Mary Reilly*? ***The Strange Case of Dr Jekyll and Mr Hyde***

100. Who was Muhammad Ali's trainer? **Angelo Dundee**

Quiz 34

1. Name the presenter of *Collectors' Lot* on TV. **Sue Cook**

2. Is noyau a brandy cordial, a silk material or a Roman Catholic ritual? **A brandy cordial**

3. Who was the Greek goddess of harvest? **Demeter**

4. Which is the only minor planet visible to the naked eye? **Vesta**

5. How many possible combinations of raised dots are there in Braille: 63, 78 or 92? **63**

6. In which novel did Adam Wayne lead a rebellion against the King of London? ***The Napoleon of Notting Hill***

7. The diagnosis of which disease is confirmed by Koplick's spots? **Measles**

8. Why were the schoolboys trying to raise money in *The Otterbury Incident*? **To pay for a broken window**

9. When is France's National Day? **July 14th**

10. How many provinces are there in the Church of England? **Two**

11. What is a urostyle? **A bone**

12. Sheikh Omar Abderahman and others were sentenced to life imprisonment for bombing which building? **World Trade Centre**

13. Who played Lynda in the film *Wish You Were Here*? **Emily Lloyd**

14. Who discovered the TB bacillus? **Robert Koch**

15. Which famous ruler attended Dutch anatomy lectures, met the British Astronomer Royal, worked in shipyards in Amsterdam and studied science? **Peter the Great**

16. In what year was there a hunger march from Glasgow to London? **1929**

17. Whom did Jenny Seagrove (and Deborah Kerr) play in the TV series *A Woman of Substance*? **Emma Harte**

18. Why was boxer Ingemar Johansson disqualified in the 1952 Olympic Heavyweight Final? **For not trying**

19. What is ustion? **The act of burning**

20. Who was searching for his lost brother in the novel *King Solomon's Mines*? **Sir Henry Curtis**

21. Which bay lies between The Machars and the Mull of Galloway? **Luce Bay**

22. Where would you find a jewel-block? **On a sailing ship**

23. True or false: a cudbear is a rat? **False (It is a dye)**

24. Where did Barry Sheene have a serious crash in 1975? **Daytona**

25. Is a twayblade a tree branch, an orchid or a battle-axe? **An orchid**

26. Who played Red Stovall in the film *Honkytonk Man*? **Clint Eastwood**

27. What kind of plane dropped the atomic bomb on Hiroshima? **A B-29**

28. What form does the trophy awarded to the winner of the British Open Golf Championship take? **A claret jug**

29. Who was the form-master of the Remove at Greyfriars School? **Mr Quelch**

30. In which activity was Henry II of France taking part when he died? **A jousting tournament**

31. Who played Big X in the film *The Great Escape*? **Richard Attenborough**

32. True or false: there is a book of Jonah in the Bible? **True**

33. What is a piddock? **A bivalve mollusc**

34. Which word means a point of argument, offspring and a publication? **Issue**

35. Who wrote *Erewhon*? **Samuel Butler**

36. Who is the Minister for the Civil Service?
The Prime Minister

37. Which Joseph Conrad character was played on TV by Claudio Amendola? *Nostromo*

38. Who had No 1 hits with *This Ole House* and *Mambo Italiano*? **Rosemary Clooney**

39. For what purpose is Paris white used? **Polishing**

40. Who played Jane Fonda's husband in the film *Coming Home*? **Bruce Dern**

41. Who, in the Bible, had wives called Sarah, Hagar and Keturah? **Abraham**

42. Who was the first man to run the 100 metres in less than 10 seconds? **Jim Hines**

43. Which Irish pop singer was awarded an honorary KBE in 1986? **Bob Geldof**

44. Which organisation's address is 16 Lancaster Gate, London? **Football Association**

45. What colour is the dye, kamala? **Orange**

46. Who wrote the operas *La Canterina*, *Mondo della Lima* and *Armida*? **Haydn**

47. Who wrote *The Shifting of the Fire*, *The Good Soldier* and the *Fifth Queen* trilogy? **Ford Madox Ford**

48. In mythology, who was the judge of the divine beauty contest won by Venus? **Paris**

49. Who played Miranda Richardson's politician husband in the film *Damage*? **Jeremy Irons**

50. Which comedian played John Parry in the TV series *Common As Muck*? **Roy Hudd**

51. Of what is histology the study? **Organic tissues**

52. Who trained *Aldaniti* when he won the Grand National?
Josh Gifford

53. True or false: Michael Chang played in two Grand Slam Men's Singles tennis finals in 1996? **True**

54. Which king of England married Philippa of Hainault and banished his mother to Castle Rising? **Edward III**

55. In which county is Frensham Heights Independent School?
Surrey

56. Who had Top Ten hits with *Rise To the Occasion* and *Love Changes Everything*? **Climie Fisher**

57. Which sport would hold a kermesse? **Cycling**

58. Which poison can be obtained from the seed nux vomica?
Strychnine

59. Who wrote *Mary Barton*, *Sylvia's Lovers* and *Cousin Phillis*? **Elizabeth Gaskell**

60. Who played the leading villain in the film *North By Northwest*? **James Mason**

61. For what does the abbreviation SFO stand?
Serious Fraud Office

62. Which political post has been held by Selwyn Lloyd, Horace King and George Thomas?
Speaker of the House of Commons

63. What was the nickname of Christopher Biggins' character in the TV series *Porridge*? **Lukewarm**

64. In which Olympic sport in 1928 did two men tie for first and three for third and no silver medal was awarded?
(Speed) skating

65. Who was appointed Astronomer Royal in 1995?

Sir Martin Rees

66. In which country was writer Roald Dahl born? **Wales**

67. Whose Top Ten hits included *Wanted, Hot Diggity* and *More*? **Perry Como**

68. Whose poetry included *The Bride of Abydos* and *The Corsair*? **Lord Byron**

69. Who directed the films *Splash, Backdraft* and *Ransom*?

Ron Howard

70. Which fruit is also called the fen-berry? **Cranberry**

71. For which constituency did writer and TV personality Gyles Brandreth become MP in 1992? **City of Chester**

72. Which ex-Australian Prime Minister became Lord Warden of the Cinque Ports in 1964? **Sir Robert Menzies**

73. Who composed the musical score for the films *Captain Blood*, *The Sea Hawk* and *The Adventures of Robin Hood*?

Erich Wolfgang Korngold

74. What was the subject of the TV series *Stuff the White Rabbit*? **Magic, illusion, etc**

75. Which British author married Frieda Von Richtofen?

D H Lawrence

76. After Len Hutton, who was the second England cricket captain to regain and retain the Ashes? **Mike Brearley**

77. How many months are there in the Sikh calendar? **12**

78. Who would use clobber in his job?
A cobbler, shoemaker (It is a paste to hide cracks)

79. Is saffian a dye, a type of leather or a herb used for flavouring? **A type of leather**

80. Who had Top Ten hits with *Hold On, My Lovin'* and
    Whatta Man?   **En Vogue**

81. True or false: there is a position called Keeper of the
    Royal Philatelic Collection?   **True**

82. Which word means a pressing crowd, an infatuation and a
    fruit drink?   **Crush**

83. In which film did Louis Gosset Jr play Sgt Emil Foley?
                                An Officer and a Gentleman

84. In TV's *Dad's Army* what was the name of Captain
    Mainwaring's wife?   **Elizabeth**

85. What shape is a crural object?   **Leg-shaped**

86. What title did Sir Anthony Eden take in 1961?
                                              Earl of Avon

87. Who printed the 42-line Bible?   **Gutenberg**

88. Which British author went to Washington as part of a
    Panamanian delegation in 1977?   **Graham Greene**

89. James Couzens was the business partner of which famous
    industrialist?   **Henry Ford**

90. In which sport was Clive Churchill known as 'The Little
    Master'?   **Rugby League**

91. What is a rest-harrow?   **A flowering plant**

92. In which city are the Bargate museum, the Weigh-house,
    God's House Tower and the Mayflower Memorial?
                                              Southampton

93. Which word means a current, a horizontal mine and a
    gradual change?   **Shift**

94. What colour is the pigment smalt?   **Blue**

95. Who played the Corsican Brothers in the film *The Corsican Brothers*?   **Douglas Fairbanks Jr**

96. What is the state capital of Pennsylvania?   **Harrisburg**

97. Who would use a fipple?   **Musician (woodwind player)**

98. Give the surname of Sanjay and Gita in TV's *Eastenders*.
                                                    Kapoor

99. In mythology, which lovers were trapped by Vulcan's impenetrable and invisible net?   **Venus and Mars**

100. Is loden an ore, unleavened bread or a woollen cloth?
                                             A woollen cloth

Quiz 35

1. Who played a dual role in the film *The Black Room*?
                                             Boris Karloff

2. With which aunt did Tom Sawyer live?   **Aunt Polly**

3. Which English navigator, half-brother of Walter Raleigh, was drowned on a voyage from Newfoundland in 1583?
                                          Sir Humphrey Gilbert

4. Who founded the Matchroom snooker organisation?
                                             Barry Hearn

5. Who was Israel's Defence Minister during the Six-day War?   **Moshe Dayan**

6. What has a recidivist done?
                            Committed a crime, been to jail

7. Which national daily newspaper has its HQ at 20 North Bridge, Edinburgh?   *The Scotsman*

8. Which English mystic set up the first American Shaker settlement at Albany in 1776?   **(Mother) Anna Lee**

9. Which writer walked from Monk's House in Sussex and committed suicide in the River Ouse? **Virginia Woolf**

10. Which word means a strong wind, a periodic payment of rent and the bog-myrtle? **Gale**

11. Who had Top Ten hits with *The Eton Rifles*, *Funeral Pyre* and *Absolute Beginners*? **The Jam**

12. Which jazz musician wrote *Nuages, Dinette* and *Crepuscule*? **Django Reinhardt**

13. Who, in the early 19th century, was known as 'The Liberator of Chile'? **Bernardo O'Higgins**

14. In which county is Chysauster Ancient Village? **Cornwall**

15. Who composed the oratorio *Israel in Egypt*? **Handel**

16. Which is the oldest English dukedom? **Norfolk**

17. Who wrote *Brothers and Sisters*, *Daughters and Sons* and *Mother and Son*? **Ivy Compton-Burnett**

18. In a Royal Salute, how many guns are fired on the anniversary of the Queen's birthday? **62**

19. Who had Top Ten hits with *Magic Touch*, *Don't Be a Fool* and *Hangin' On a String*? **Loose Ends**

20. True or false: the M9 runs from Edinburgh to Carlisle? **False (Edinburgh to Stirling)**

21. Which football team, First Division champions in 1937, were relegated in 1938 despite having scored more goals than the new champions? **Manchester City**

22. Which 1995 film was subtitled *The Adventure Home*? *Free Willy 2*

23. Of what is nostology the study? **Senility and second childhood**

24. In Roman numerals what number is represented when a bar is over VI? **6,000**

25. In the 1934 film *Babes In Toyland*, who were Santa's inept assistants? **Laurel and Hardy**

26. Name the sport associated with the TV series *The Morning Line*. **Horse-racing**

27. Who wrote *A Journal of the Plague Year* and *Colonel Jack*? **Daniel Defoe**

28. Which areas are connected by an isocheim? **Areas of same winter temperature**

29. What were trous-de-loup? **Pits as a defence against cavalry**

30. Who was the first king of England to die in 1066? **Edward the Confessor**

31. Who had Top Twenty hits with *Breathe Again* and *Another Sad Song*? **Toni Braxton**

32. Which seeds give the flavouring to the liqueur kummel? **Caraway seeds**

33. From which Welsh club did Celtic sign Jock Stein as a player? **Llanelli**

34. The red clay, abraum, is used to deepen the colour of which wood? **Mahogany**

35. Who played the title role in the film *Carbine Williams*? **James Stewart**

36. What is Prince Charles' RAF rank? **Group Captain**

37. True or false: Victor Francis Hess was an American physicist? **True**

38. What do creatures do when they nidificate? **Build nests**

39. Who wrote *The Spy*, *The Pilot* and *The Prairie*?
James Fenimore Cooper

40. On TV what was the name of Alf Garnett's daughter?
Rita

41. Who designed the locomotives *Silver Jubilee*, *Coronation* and *The Mallard*? **Sir Nigel Gresley**

42. Into what is the Greek drachma divided? **100 leptae**

43. Is a girouette a dance step, a weather-cock or a precious stone? **A weather-cock**

44. Who wrote *The Bull From the Sea* and *The Persian Boy*?
Mary Renault

45. Who would be carried in a cacolet?
Sick or wounded people

46. Which South African Test bowler was nicknamed 'Toey'?
Hugh Tayfield

47. How many Great Livery Companies are there? **12**

48. Which South American capital city is virtually on the Equator? **Quito**

49. Who starred in the films *My Brilliant Career*, *A Passage To India* and *Kangaroo*? **Judy Davis**

50. Whom did Frank Bruno defeat to win boxing's WBC Heavyweight Title? **Oliver McCall**

51. Who had Top Ten hits with *Can't I, Ramblin' Rose* and *Dreams Can Tell a Lie*? **Nat 'King' Cole**

52. Which shipping forecast area is to the west of Biscay?
Finisterre

53. Where would a musician find a posaune? **On an organ**

54. If someone was your 'Achates', what would he be?
A trusted friend

55. Why is wood kyanised? **To prevent dry-rot**

56. Is kwashiorkor a disease, a Russian emblem or a unit of currency? **A disease**

57. Of which 1939 film was the 1956 film *Storm Over the Nile* a re-make? ***The Four Feathers***

58. Name the actor playing Superintendent Mallett in TV's *A Touch of Frost*. **Bruce Alexander**

59. On what was Edmond Hoyle first an authority?
Card games

60. What name did Nicolas Breakspear assume as Pope?
Adrian (IV)

61. From what is the drink kumiss (koumiss) made?
Fermented mare's milk

62. True or false: the population of the Falkland Isles is less than 2,000? **False (2,000+)**

63. Which industrialist tried to negotiate a European peace in 1915 by chartering a 'Peace Ship' to Europe?
Henry Ford

64. Who had a 1985 No 1 hit with *You Spin Me Round*?
Dead or Alive

65. Is a hask a basket, a clamp or a preparation made from horns? **A basket**

66. What are the Beefsteak, Lansdowne, Alpine and Savage?
London clubs

67. Which film made a star of Claude Rains although he was only on screen for the last minute or so?
The Invisible Man

68. Which TV series featured the characters John Loengard and Kimberley Sayers? **Dark Skies**

69. Who wore a sagum? **Roman soldiers (It is a cloak)**

70. Who were the hundred men in the film *One Hundred Men and a Girl*? **Musicians**

71. Who wrote *Alton Locke* and *Hypatia*? **Charles Kingsley**

72. Which word means a plan, a small piece of land and to scald? **Plot**

73. In which British city is the Arnolfini gallery? **Bristol**

74. The Gulf of Riga is off the coast of which country? **Latvia**

75. Who fashioned the bronze sculpture *Perseus With the Head of Medusa*? **Cellini**

76. At the end of 1996, how many countries were members of the UN: 162, 176 or 185? **185**

77. Who would use a scotograph? **A blind person**

78. Who had Top Ten hits with *Really Saying Something*, *Tunnel of Love* and *Our Lips Are Sealed*? **Fun Boy Three**

79. What term is used to describe a quarter bottle of wine? **A nip**

80. Which former England captain became manager of Arsenal in 1962? **Billy Wright**

81. Which garden flower is also called the rose-mallow? **Hollyhock**

82. Did R A F de Réaumur invent a thermometer, the kaleidoscope or the stethoscope? **A thermometer**

83. Which film's advertising slogan was "Don't give away the ending – it's the only one we have."? **Psycho**

84. With which instrument would you associate Diderik Buxtehude? **The organ**

85. Who, in the Bible, was the father of Joshua? **Nun**

86. Four US states border Mexico: New Mexico, California and Texas are three. What is the fourth? **Arizona**

87. Geographically, what is odd about a how and a howe? **They are opposites (a hill and a valley)**

88. Which two words started film titles that ended *Animal House, Christmas Vacation* and *Class Reunion*? **National Lampoon's**

89. Who had Top Ten hits with *Hi-Fidelity* and *Starmaker*? **Kids from 'Fame'**

90. Which former amount of money was known as a 'bull'? **Five shillings**

91. Which element has the chemical symbol Sb? **Antimony**

92. Which breed of dog is also known as the badger-dog? **Dachshund**

93. What is a ladrone? **A thief, highwayman**

94. In Palestine from 1946 to 1948 what was Irgun? **A Jewish guerilla group**

95. Who introduced the TV series *Put It To The Test*? **Carol Vorderman**

96. Jackie Stewart retired from motor-racing after the death of which team mate in 1973? **Francois Cevert**

97. Who created the Moomintrolls? **Tove Jansson**

98. Who was saved by a 'long count' and went on to retain the World Heavyweight Boxing Title? **Gene Tunney**

99. Who was the first cricketer to take 11 catches in a Test Match? **Jack Russell**

100. Who played the insurance investigator in the film *The Thomas Crown Affair*? **Faye Dunaway**

Quiz 36

1. Who would use abb in his work? **A weaver**

2. Who created the literary characters Count Fathom, Sir Launcelot Greaves and Humphrey Clinker?
Tobias Smollett

3. What is measured by the cgs unit the gilbert?
Magneto-motive force

4. Which Pidgin English expression means 'at once', 'quickly'? **Chop chop**

5. Which city uses an anchor on its hallmarks?
Birmingham

6. For what does the abbreviation CH stand?
Companion of Honour

7. What are Emperor, Grand Eagle and Colombier?
Paper sizes

8. For which creature was a rearmouse an old name? **A bat**

9. Who had Top Ten hits with *Kiss, Sway* and *Return To Me*? **Dean Martin**

10. Who played the title role in the film *Mahler*?
Robert Powell

11. Is an emys a growth on a bone, a freshwater tortoise or a Greek magistrate? **Tortoise**

12. What is the opposite of a bimbo? **A himbo**

13. Who played Mrs Jessop in the TV series *Woof*? **Liza Goddard**

14. Who would have used a lapstone in his job? **A shoemaker**

15. What was the nickname of US politician Huey Long? **Kingfish**

16. True or false: a printer's ream has more sheets than an ordinary ream of paper? **True**

17. Which word means a bar of wood, to use abusive language and a bird? **Rail**

18. What is rémoulade? **A sauce**

19. Which Shakespeare role has been played on film by Nicol Williamson, Mel Gibson and Innokenti Smoktunovsky? **Hamlet**

20. From where does Radio Wave operate? **Blackpool**

21. What condition is caused by kerion? **Baldness**

22. Who was the first unseeded tennis player to win the Wimbledon Men's Singles Title? **Boris Becker**

23. What was the subject of the TV series *House To House*? **Politics**

24. Who had Top Ten hits with *You Got Soul*, *Cupid* and *Hold me Tight*? **Johnny Nash**

25. Which famous author was a smuggler, a sea captain, a failed suicide and explored the Congo? **Joseph Conrad**

26. Who, at the 1984 Olympics, equalled Jesse Owens' record of four gold athletics medals? **Carl Lewis**

27. Which poetic name for Britain was derived from the Latin for 'white'? **Albion**

28. What is the other name for cabinet pudding? **Chancellor's Pudding**

29. Is Cabora Bassa a Spanish dance, an Italian opera singer or an African dam? **An African dam**

30. Were jougs a form of punishment, lees from whiskey making or spurs? **A form of punishment (They are an iron collar and chain)**

31. Which word means a sudden stop, a test for accuracy and a cross-lined pattern? **Check**

32. In which film did Robin Williams play Professor John Keating? ***Dead Poets' Society***

33. Is a killdee an antelope, a bird or a small boat? **A bird**

34. Who designed Kedleston Hall, Kenwood House and Culzean Castle? **Robert Adam**

35. Which British city did Robert Louis Stevenson describe as "a crumbling human pigsty fit for pigs"? **Edinburgh**

36. Which notorious murderer had the first names Hawley Harvey? **Dr Crippen**

37. Who banged the gong in the 'Yes-No' interlude of TV's original *Take Your Pick*? **Alec Dane**

38. Who were the Admiral's Men? **A group of actors (in Elizabethan times)**

39. What is the other name of the Rio Grande? **Rio Bravo**

40. What, in Scotland, is the Black Isle? **A promontory**

41. Who played the blackmailer in the 1957 film *The Naked Truth*? **Dennis Price**

42. True or false: William Wordsworth never met Oscar Wilde? **True**

43. Where would you find a voussoir: in a telescope, in a café or in an arch? **In an arch**

44. Who wrote the plays *Our Betters*, *The Unknown* and *East of Suez*? **W Somerset Maugham**

45. Which TV series was set in Verenmoor open prison? ***Insiders***

46. With which country were the Morley-Minto reforms concerned? **India**

47. Is lametta a type of cheese, volcanic rock or gold or silver wire? **Gold or silver wire**

48. Which player-manager of Glasgow Rangers was sent off in his first match in 1986? **Graham Souness**

49. At which battle did Edward, the Black Prince, 'win his spurs'? **Crécy**

50. For what purpose did the Romans use a lanx: to measure distance, to serve meat or to illuminate houses? **To serve meat (It was a platter)**

51. Of what is an advouter guilty? **Adultery**

52. In Muslim mythology, what was an Afreet? **Demon, monster**

53. On what is Aich's Metal used? **Ships' bottoms**

54. As what was Matthew Modine re-incarnated in the film *Fluke*? **A dog**

55. Of which alphabet is 'aleph' the first letter? **Hebrew**

56. Is agnus castus a disease of sheep, disbelief in God or an aromatic shrub? **An aromatic shrub**

57. Which spice is prepared from the berry of the pimento?
Allspice

58. Which vegetable is affected by anbury, the disease known as 'fingers and toes'? **Turnip**

59. After the TV series *Vision On,* Tony Hart got his own series: what was it called? ***Take Hart***

60. If ursine means bearlike and porcine piglike, what does anguline mean? **Snakelike**

61. Which large island is known as Apple Island by the country's people? **Tasmania**

62. What is the purpose of an argyle on a dinner-table?
To keep gravy hot

63. Which organisation's motto is "Maintain the Right"?
Royal Canadian Mounted Police

64. What do aphyllous plants lack: leaves, roots or flowers?
Leaves

65. Which word means a diagonal parting in coal, to support and a defender in football? **Back**

66. Which game is central to the film *Innocent Moves*?
Chess

67. What is estimated by an algometer? **Sensitivity to pain**

68. In the examinations known as A/S Levels, what does A/S stand for? **Advanced Supplementary**

69. Which part of the body is affected by labyrinthitis?
The inner ear

70. Who narrated the radio series *Vivat Rex*?
Richard Burton

71. Which duo had a TV show with a segment called *Beat the Barber*? **Ant and Dec**

72. Who would use badigeon in their work?
Sculptors and builders (It is a substance for filling in holes)

73. Who wore a laticlave as a mark of rank?
Roman senators

74. In which sport might you use a lutz? **Figure-skating**

75. Which meteorological feature was once called levin?
Lightning

76. Is a launce a boat, a sand-eel or a dance? **A sand-eel**

77. How many Vestal Virgins were there? **Six**

78. Who would have letters of credence? **A diplomat**

79. In World War II what name was given to the American mass-produced, prefabricated cargo-ships? **Liberty ships**

80. Which word means a flat-bottom boat, not as heavy and an igniting pocket-appliance? **Lighter**

81. True or false: an undine was a soul-less water sprite?
True

82. According to Shakespeare, when would a man be in liver-vein? **When in love**

83. Is lithoplane a surgical procedure, ornamental porcelain or stone-carving? **Ornamental porcelain**

84. Which English batsman was dismissed only once in scoring 212 runs against New Zealand in the Final Test of 1997? **Mike Atherton**

85. Who on TV had a garden called Barleywood?
Alan Titchmarsh

86. Is a logogryph a word-puzzle, a religious inscription or a lie-detector? **A word-puzzle**

87. What colour is the pigment verditer? **Light blue**

88. Of what is a torr a unit? **Pressure**

89. Which poem begins "Behold! A giant am I!"?
The Windmill

90. What is the common word for the condition calivity?
Baldness

91. When are carcakes eaten in Scotland?
On Shrove Tuesday

92. There are four cardinal signs of the zodiac: Aries, Libra and Cancer are three – what is the fourth? **Capricorn**

93. Which word means a squint, a mould and a throw of dice?
Cast

94. In which US state does the Daytona 500 race take place?
Florida

95. What does a toril gateway lack? **A gate!**

96. How many sheaves make a thrave: 20, 24 or 36? **24**

97. Which Shakespearean character had a horse called Capilet? **Sir Andrew Aguecheek**

98. What is detected by a sideroscope?
Degrees of magnetism

99. True or false: tutty is cheap woollen cloth?
False (It is an oxide of zinc)

100. Which continental ballet company was developed by British choreographer John Cranko? **Stuttgart Ballet**

Quiz 37

1. What was the purpose of 'pink noise' recordings?
To soothe babies

2. In literature which boy was recruited by Colonel Creighton to act as a spy? **Kim**

3. What meat should be in a carbonnade? **Beef**

4. What is the abbreviation for Bachelor of Surgery? **ChB**

5. In which sport would you use a cockabondy?
   Angling (It is an artificial fly)

6. Which stretch of water separates West Falkland from East Falkland? **Falkland Sound**

7. Which productive creatures live in a magnanerie?
   Silkworms

8. Who said of the US Ryder Cup team: "The American team were 11 nice guys and Paul Azinger."?
   Seve Ballesteros

9. In which bay are the Aran Islands? **Galway Bay**

10. Where would you find machair: just above the high-water mark, on mountain slopes or on forest floors?
    Just above the high-water mark

11. Is a loupe a female wolf, a scowl or a magnifying-glass?
    A magnifying-glass

12. True or false: a cattalo is a cross between domestic cattle and a bison? **True**

13. Which vehicle was launched by Sir Clive Sinclair on March 4th, 1992? **The Zike**

14. Which word is used in printing to describe the blurred impression which causes printed matter to appear double: mackle, bioptid or pingle? **Mackle**

15. What is the common name for methylenedioxymethamphetamine? **Ecstasy**

16. Who said of Warren Beatty: "He's 50 from the neck up and 14 from the waist down."? **Shirley Maclaine**

17. Who appeared in the films *Urban Cowboy*, *Pulp Fiction* and *Get Shorty*? **John Travolta**

18. In *Coronation Street,* who bought Alma's share of Jim's Café? **Roy Cropper**

19. Which medal did Torvill and Dean win at the 1994 Olympics? **Bronze**

20. Which Dorset village is famous for a great tithe barn, a swannery, famous gardens and a ceremony to mark the start of the mackerel season? **Abbotsbury**

21. Who in fiction was the famous husband of Badroulboudour? **Aladdin**

22. Henry Bishop wrote more than 80 operas, but is chiefly remembered for which famous sentimental song?
Home, Sweet Home

23. Which word means a simple catch in cricket, a stick used to agitate clothes in a wash-tub and a child's toy? **Dolly**

24. Who played Tammy Wynette in the film *Stand By Your Man*? **Annette O'Toole**

25. Is a herdic a horse-drawn carriage, a sheep-pen or an ancient monument? **A horse-drawn carriage**

26. Who played Macheath in the 1952 film *The Beggar's Opera*? **Laurence Olivier**

27. Who presented the TV series *Brass Eye*? **Chris Morris**

28. Which identification system was brought to Britain in 1901 by Sir Edward Henry? **Fingerprinting**

29. In Botany, what is meant by 'gemmate'? **Having buds**

30. Who wrote *Crome Yellow*, *Brief Candles* and *After Many a Stop*? **Aldous Huxley**

31. Which English batsman scored 456 runs in a Test Match in 1990? **Graham Gooch**

32. In the film *Darkman* how long did the liquid skin last in the light before disintegrating? **99 minutes**

33. With which objects was the game of conkers originally played?
Snail shells (It took its name from the Latin for shell – concha)

34. Was the Automobile Association founded in 1895, 1900 or 1905? **1905**

35. What was Desperate Dan's favourite food? **Cow pies**

36. Traditionally, what size was an allotment?
A quarter of an acre

37. Who was the art editor and illustrator of *The Yellow Book*?
Aubrey Beardsley

38. Who played Reg Varney's sister in TV's *On the Buses*?
Anna Karen

39. Which popular film's last line was "You just ain't ready for me yet."? *The Cincinnati Kid*

40. Which country's official name is Eesti Vabariik?
Estonia's

41. In which English town is Hall i' th' Wood and the Tonge Moor Textile Museum? **Bolton**

42. Who played Robin Hood in the film *Sword of Sherwood Forest*? **Richard Greene**

43. How many playing cards are used in the game of écarté?
32

44. Which famous author's mother wrote under the name 'Speranza'? **Oscar Wilde's**

45. What colour was the second penny stamp? **Red**

46. Where is the Bass Rock? **In the Firth of Forth**

47. Which heavyweight boxing champion was described as "a tulip among the weeds"? **Mike Tyson**

48. True or false: Stuart Lane played in every match for the British Lions on the 1980 tour of South Africa? **False (He played only 45 seconds of the first match)**

49. Who led the Labour Party from 1935 to 1955? **Clement Attlee**

50. Which character journeyed in time and space in the TV series *Quantum Leap*? **Sam Beckett**

51. Which radio programme began "Are you sitting comfortably?"? *Listen With Mother*

52. With which Greek god is the Cerne Abbas Giant associated? **Hercules**

53. In which county is Portchester Castle? **Hampshire**

54. Which dance was described in 1990 as "a fast-paced dance performed with the man's right leg placed between the thighs of his partner."? **The Lambada**

55. Who played Mr Crocker-Harris in the film *The Browning Version*? **Michael Redgrave**

56. In which country was Rudyard Kipling born? **India**

57. Which is the only Commonwealth country with territory inside the Arctic Circle? **Canada**

58. Who wrote *That Uncertain Feeling*, *Take a Girl Like You* and *Ending Up*? **Kingsley Amis**

59. Which 'bird' name was given to the squalid areas of 19th century London where the poor huddled together?

Rookeries

60. What is the equivalent army rank of a naval Chief Petty Officer?

Staff sergeant

61. Who lost an Olympic gold medal because of stanozolol?

Ben Johnson

62. Which bird is called a deviling in some parts of Britain?

The swift

63. Which song character was a High Churchman, a Papist, a man of no principles, a Tory and a Whig?

The Vicar of Bray

64. Who compèred the TV show *Stars and Garters*?

Ray Martine

65. Who played the professional assassin in the film *The Green Man*?

Alastair Sim

66. What was the Christian name of 'Papa Doc' Duvalier?

François

67. In which English resort was the film *A Chorus of Disapproval* set?

Scarborough

68. Was a cottier a peasant, a small farmhouse or a weaver?

A peasant

69. In the hymn *All Things Bright and Beautiful* which line follows "The rich man in his castle"?

The poor man at his gate

70. Which member of the Royal Family gave evidence in the notorious Baccarat Scandal trial of 1891?

The Prince of Wales

71. What was engineer Joseph Bazalgette's important contribution to the improvement of London? **The sewers**

72. Who wrote and illustrated *Father Christmas*, *Fungus the Bogeyman* and *Where the Wind Blows*?

Raymond Briggs

73. Which football club was intended to be merged with Oxford United to form the Thames Valley Royals?

Reading

74. When does the official trout fishing season begin?

March 1st

75. Who played Bob Hoskins' best friend in the TV series *Thick as Thieves*? **John Thaw**

76. Is a carronade a volley of artillery, a small carriage or a short cannon? **A short cannon**

77. Who played the exiled king in the film *A King In New York*? **Charlie Chaplin**

78. Who wrote *The Newcomers*, *The Rose and the Ring* and *The History of Henry Esmond Esquire*? **W M Thackeray**

79. Which lady from Plymouth is famous for her paintings of large ladies in humorous settings? **Beryl Cook**

80. In which city is there a D-Day Museum containing the Overlord embroidery? **Portsmouth**

81. Which word means a torch, a connecting part and one hundredth of a chain? **Link**

82. Which novelist was appointed Chief Surveyor of the eastern counties by the Post Office? **Anthony Trollope**

83. Is a bise a drinking-glass, a wind or a biscuit? **A wind**

84. True or false: the Abbey National originated in London's Abbey Road? **True**

85. What did Wormold sell in *Our Man in Havana*?

Vacuum-cleaners

86. Who played Wing Commander Yeo-Thomas in the TV series *The White Rabbit*? **Kenneth More**

87. What is the common word used to describe trees or plants that are sempervirent? **Evergreen**

88. Which TV announcer played private eye Mark Saber on TV? **Donald Gray**

89. Who had Top Ten hits with *Come As You Are, Smells Like Teen Spirit* and *Heart-Shaped Box*? **Nirvana**

90. What are Safar, Rajab, Mubarram, Jumada I and Jumada II? **Months in the Muslim calendar**

91. Who played the female lead in the film *Ash Wednesday*? **Elizabeth Taylor**

92. Is trolly an alloy, a kind of lace or jovial singing? **A kind of lace**

93. Which musician composed *The Song of Hiawatha* trilogy? **Samuel Coleridge-Taylor**

94. What was unusual about Joseph Filliston when he umpired the Lords Taverners v Old England match at Lords in 1962? **He was 100 years old!**

95. Who said: "It takes two to speak the truth – one to speak and the other to hear."? **Henry Thoreau**

96. In which famous book, later filmed, did General Groundwort appear? ***Watership Down***

97. Who is Colonel-in-Chief of the Guards regiments? **HM the Queen**

98. Which word means a junction between two parts, hog's lard and a measure equal to 8 bushels? **Seam**

99. Which country's flag bears the motto *Ordem e Progresso*? **Brazil's**

100. Who played the lead in the TV drama series *Out*?

Tom Bell

Quiz 38

1. Who had a 1980 No 1 hit with *Use It Up and Wear It Out*?
Odyssey

2. What was the name of George Kennedy's character in the film *Cool Hand Luke*?
Dragline

3. In the US Civil War who led the famous 'March to the Sea'?
General W T Sherman

4. Which title was first conferred on a daughter of Charles II about 1642?
Princess Royal

5. True or false: Chile is the only commercial producer of nitrate of soda from natural resources?
True

6. What is a fish-gig?
A barbed spear

7. On which form of transport would you find an eta patch?
A balloon

8. Who, in 1964, won an FA Cup winner's medal with West Ham Utd and was a member of Worcestershire's County Championship winning side?
Jim Standen

9. What is the central theme of Milton's *Paradise Regained*?
Christ's Temptation by Satan

10. Who was the man who saved many wounded soldiers on a donkey at Gallipoli?
James Simpson Fitzpatrick

11. What did Christopher Columbus use to demonstrate that once he showed the way then others would follow?
An egg

12. Which famous woodcarver was appointed by Charles II to the Board of Works and employed in the chapel at Windsor? **Grinling Gibbons**

13. Of which bay is the Andaman Sea a part? **Bay of Bengal**

14. Who was the first golfer to score four sub-70 rounds in the US Open? **Lee Trevino**

15. With which helpful organisation is Dame Cicely Mary Saunders associated? **The hospice movement**

16. Who played the title role in the film *Cash McCall*? **James Garner**

17. Of which US state is Jefferson City the capital? **Missouri**

18. Which of these capital cities is NOT a seaport: Helsinki, Colombo, Phnom Penh or Ankara? **Ankara**

19. In which film did a tobacco company offer $24 million to any town which could stop smoking for 30 days? ***Cold Turkey***

20. Who sculpted the statue of Captain R F Scott which stands in Waterloo Place, London? **His widow, Lady Kathleen Scott**

21. What is the subject of Thomas Hardy's epic *The Dynasts*? **The war with Napoleon**

22. In which county are Lullingstone Roman Villa, Penshurst Place and Richborough Castle? **Kent**

23. In which event did South African Josiah Thugwane win an Olympic gold medal in 1996? **The Marathon**

24. What was the No 1 hit for *Spitting Image*? ***The Chicken Song***

25. What, in Europe in the 19th century, was the Zollverein?
A customs union

26. Which brothers played the brothers in the film *The Fabulous Baker Boys*? **Jeff and Beau Bridges**

27. In which play, by John van Druten, did witch Gillian Holroyd have a cat called Pyewacket?
Bell, Book and Candle

28. What are *Apollo*, *Granta*, *The Lady* and *Mizz*?
Magazines

29. What connects a shepherd loved by the goddess Diana, a long poem by Keats and a novel by Disraeli? *Endymion*

30. Would you use a trommel for cleaning fibres, measuring earth tremors or cleaning and sizing ore?
Cleaning and sizing ore

31. Whose only No 1 hit was *Hey Girl Don't Bother Me*?
The Tams

32. Which Indian nobleman, known as the Black Prince of Cricketers, played for Sussex and England?
K S Ranjitsinhji

33. In which Sir Walter Scott novel does the blind fiddler Wandering Willie appear? *Redgauntlet*

34. In which island country is Mindanao? **The Philippines**

35. Which classic film told the story of *HMS Torrin* and its crew? *In Which We Serve*

36. True or false: one cubic foot of water weighs more than 70 pounds? **False (62.32 lbs)**

37. Who had Top Ten hits with *Suddenly*, *Red Light Spells Danger* and *Get Outta My Dreams Get Into My Car*?
Billy Ocean

38. Who in 1823 patented and developed James Symes' method of waterproofing? **Charles MacIntosh**

39. Which English club did Jock Stein manage in 1978? **Leeds United**

40. What is the capital of Belarus? **Minsk**

41. Which word means to cause to take wing, a sudden flow of water and to blush? **Flush**

42. Which famous building occupies the site of the old Montagu House in Bloomsbury, London? **British Museum**

43. What would be the occupation of someone with the letters FRCR after their name? **Radiologist**

44. Who had Top Ten hits with *Everything About You* and *Cats in the Cradle*? **Ugly Kid Joe**

45. Who played the chorus girl who became the show-saving leading lady in the classic film musical *42nd Street*? **Ruby Keeler**

46. What was a schläger? **A duelling sword**

47. In which London street is the Stock Exchange? **Old Broad Street**

48. After what is the pantomime character Widow Twankey named? **Green tea (Twankay)**

49. Who played the theatrical agent in the film *The Girl Can't Help It*? **Tom Ewell**

50. Which horse, owned by the Prince of Wales, won the 1896 Derby? *Persimmon*

51. Who, after a shipwreck, reached land on a plank and later, in 1477, sailed '100 leagues beyond Thule'? **Christopher Columbus**

52. In which month were the Queen Mother, Princess Margaret and Princess Anne all born? **August**

53. In human medicine, to what use is warfarin, the rodent poison, put? **Prevention of blood-clotting**

54. Who presented the 1959-60 TV game show *Spot the Tune*? **Jackie Rae**

55. What nationality was World Boxing champion Carlos Monzon? **Argentinian**

56. Who designed the uniform of the Pope's bodyguard, the Swiss Guard? **Michelangelo**

57. Who brought Pinocchio to life? **The Blue Fairy**

58. Which comedy actor and writer appeared in the films *Shalako, One Way Pendulum* and *Theatre of Blood*? **Eric Sykes**

59. Which TV station owner signed up 35 of the world's leading cricketers in 1977? **Kerry Packer**

60. Which poet created the club-loving cat Bustopher Jones? **T S Eliot**

61. Who played the title role in the film *Pimpernel Smith*? **Leslie Howard**

62. Who would use a godet: a dressmaker, a silver miner or a gardener? **A dressmaker**

63. Which saint's cross is decribed heraldically as 'saltire gules in a field argent'? **St Patrick's**

64. Which TV series had episodes called *Royal Jelly, Back for Christmas, Proof of Guilt* and *Georgy Porgy*? **Tales of the Unexpected**

65. What happened when the Irish Rugby team arrived in Fiji in 1976 to play Fiji? **Nothing – the Fijian team was away on tour!**

66. What is the more common name for uranology?

Astronomy

67. What is unusual about Mount Athos, a holy mountain dedicated to the Virgin Mary?

No women are allowed to set foot on it

68. Who wrote the novels *Esther Waters*, *A Modern Lover* and *Sister Teresa*? **George Moore**

69. In Egyptian mythology what form does the god Sebek take? **A crocodile**

70. Who composed the operas *Der Sturm* and *Monsieur de Pourceaugnac*? **Frank Martin**

71. Who was the first ex-US President to die in the 20th century? **Benjamin Harrison**

72. What was Mel Tormé's only UK Top Ten hit?

Mountain Greenery

73. In the film *The Taking of Pelham 123* what was Pelham 123? **A subway train**

74. True or false: Kent Cap is a breed of canary?

False (It was a paper size)

75. If you were a flaneur, would you be a flatterer, an idler or a culinary expert? **An idler**

76. In which German mountains might you see the Spectre of the Brocken? **Harz Mountains**

77. Who played Nick Charles in the 1950s TV series *The Thin Man*? **Peter Lawford**

78. Which was the first football club to have artificial turf in 1981? **Queen's Park Rangers**

79. Is a didapper a bird, a linen shirt or a tinker? **A bird**

80. Which Prime Minister wrote *The Blast of War*, *Tides of Fortune* and *Riding the Storm*?   **Harold MacMillan**

81. Who created Daffy Duck and Screwy Squirrel?
    Tex Avery

82. As what was Sir Bernard Spilsbury famous?
    A pathologist/forensic scientist

83. What was cricketer Don Bradman's middle name?
    George

84. What relation was Edward VII to Haakon VII of Norway?
    Father-in-law

85. Who played John McVicar in the film *McVicar*?
    Roger Daltrey

86. True or false: Eva Peron was President of Argentina?
    False

87. In which north east town did the Venerable Bede spend most of his life?   **Jarrow**

88. Who composed *L'Enfant Prodigue*, *La Mer* and *Images*?
    Claude Debussy

89. What nationality was the creator of Tintin?   **Belgian**

90. In which capital city was Leon Trotsky assassinated?
    Mexico City

91. Whose albums have included *Empty Sky*, *Tumbleweed Connection* and *A Single Man*?   **Elton John's**

92. Apart from his governmental powers, what did Emperor Hirohito renounce in 1946?   **His divinity**

93. Which was the first sport to be presented on British ITV?
    Boxing

94. Who wrote *The Apparition of One Mrs Veal*, *Captain Singleton* and *Colonel Jack*?   **Daniel Defoe**

95. Where did Scipio finally defeat Hannibal in 202 BC?

Zama

96. In Greek legend who married his mother Jocasta?

Oedipus

97. Which all-time great all-round sportswoman broke the world record for the high jump in the 1932 Olympics but was disqualified for using the then new Western Roll?

'Babe' (Mildred) Didrikson (Zaharias)

98. Who played the British secret agent in South America in the TV series *Top Secret*? **William Franklyn**

99. Which surname connects a US President, a famous Shakespearean scholar, an American pianist-bandleader and an explorer who died with Captain Scott? **Wilson**

100. Which one word means a portion, to divide and an actor's role? **Part**

Quiz 39

1. Which British statesman founded Oxford scholarships for Commonwealth and US students? **Cecil Rhodes**

2. Which famous British scientist's home and laboratory were burned down by a mob in 1791? **Joseph Priestley's**

3. Smoky, yellow, milky, rose and ghost are all types of which mineral silica? **Quartz**

4. Who played the lead in the film *Liar Liar*? **Jim Carrey**

5. Which word means the nap of velvet, a heap and a foundation timber? **Pile**

6. Who played Caroline in TV's *Caroline in the City*?

Lea Thompson

7.   Which part of the world was explored by John Ross, Matt Henson and Floyd Bennett?   **The Arctic**

8.   With which sport would you associate Allison Fisher?
                                                        Snooker

9.   Who had a No 1 hit with *Angel Fingers* in 1973?
                                                        Wizzard

10. Is a shanny a sheared sheep, a snake or a fish?   **A fish**

11. Who wrote *Little Boy Lost*, *The Village* and *The Victorian Chaise-Longue*?   **Marghanita Laski**

12. Which country's 1905 rugby union team were called 'The Originals'?   **New Zealand's**

13. What is the general and inclusive name for accents, umlauts, cedillas, etc?   **Diacritic (Diacritical) marks**

14. What does a doctor do when he auscultates?
                               Listens to a patient's insides/heart

15. Who played Bernard Woolley in TV's *Yes, Minister*?
                                                    Derek Fowlds

16. Who had a 1974 No 1 hit with *Sad Sweet Dreamer*?
                                                  Sweet Sensation

17. For what would you use a dibble?
                      To make holes in the ground (for seeds, etc)

18. What did Marty McFly call himself when he went back to the Wild West in the film *Back To the Future III*?
                                                    Clint Eastwood

19. In which country did the Arcos raid of May 1927 take place?   **United Kingdom**

20. Which word means an interval of silence in music, repose and a support for a cue?   **Rest**

21. Who was the first overseas player to win a Wimbledon tennis title? **May Sutton**

22. Who wrote *I, Robot* and *Caves of Steel*? **Isaac Asimov**

23. Matt Molloy and Paddy Molony were leading lights of which Irish band that performed for the Pope in 1979? **The Chieftains**

24. Is a pung a Tibetan coin, a New Zealand fern or a horse-drawn sled? **Horse-drawn sled**

25. After what did Captain Cook name the Society Islands? **The Royal Society**

26. What was the name of the jewel thief played by Liza Goddard in the TV series *Bergerac*? **Philippa Vale**

27. True or false: Baron Karl von Munchausen, narrator of exaggerated exploits, was a real person? **True (1720-97)**

28. Who sang with Roger Whittaker on the Top Ten hit *The Skye Boat Song*? **Des O'Connor**

29. True or false: Superman is an only child? **True**

30. For what purpose would you use a tedder: to spread hay in the sun, to cut the ends off weaving or to plait rope? **To spread hay in the sun**

31. Which city in Alaska, site of Elmendorf Air Base and Fort Richardson, is a key centre for oil and gas? **Anchorage**

32. Who provided the voice for cartoon character Mr Magoo? **Jim Backus**

33. Whose Top Twenty hits included *Three, Boing!* and *Sticky*? **Wedding Present**

34. Which English football club were League Champions five times in the 1930s? **Arsenal**

35. What is on the other side of the famous Buffalo nickel?
A Red Indian's head

36. Which country's rulers wore the uraeus?
Ancient Egypt's (Serpent head-dress)

37. Of which African country is Ge'ez the classicial literary language?
Ethiopia

38. Who played Alex Marsden in TV's *The Heart Surgeon*?
Nigel Havers

39. Which modern form of transport was originally called a 'pedestrian curricle'?
Bicycle

40. Who is the central character in the Candleford trilogy of stories?
Laura

41. In the film *Super Mario Bros* what was the Bros' occupation?
Plumbers

42. What was the former name of the US Presidential retreat, Camp David?
Shangri-La

43. What did astronaut Scott Carpenter descibe as "spectacular, like a very brilliant rainbow"?
Sunset seen from orbit

44. To what does the adjective 'rhinal' refer?
The nose

45. Who composed *Fanfare For the Common Man*?
Aaron Copland

46. What do merlons and crenels combine to form?
An embattled parapet

47. What colour is the cloth known as Oxford Mixture?
Dark-grey

48. Which famous town is virtually dead centre of Australia?
Alice Springs

49. Who had 1950s Top Ten hits with *Eternally, Chain Gang* and *More*? **Jimmy Young**

50. In which country were boyars the highest order of nobility? **Russia**

51. Of whom did golfer Ed Fiori say (in 1986) "I wouldn't care if I got beat by 20 shots. I'd still like to see how God does it." **Jack Nicklaus**

52. Who played Julius Caesar in the film *Caesar and Cleopatra*? **Claude Rains**

53. Who were given the vote in 1965 in Australia? **Aborigines**

54. Who wrote *The Fall*, *The Myth of Sisyphus* and *The Rebel*? **Albert Camus**

55. What is the popular name for Bach's 2nd Movement from his 3rd Orchestral Suite in D (rearranged by Wilhelmj)? ***Air On a G String***

56. Two footballers each scored four goals in England's 10-0 defeat of Portugal in 1947: name one. **Stan Mortensen or Tommy Lawton**

57. Which detective featured in the stories *The Tragedy of X, The Tragedy of Y* and *The Tragedy of Z*? **Drury Lane**

58. For what purpose is a hot-wall used? **To assist in ripening fruit trees**

59. Who played the title role in the 1944 film *Laura*? **Gene Tierney**

60. Which word means a clasp or buckle, the setting of a gem and an expression of sudden pain? **Ouch**

61. How many countries border Ecuador? **Two**

62. Where would you find alula with primary and secondary coverts? **On a bird's wing**

63. True or false: an egger is a man who gathers eggs? **True**

64. In which country was the TV series *Riders of the Dawn* set? **Spain**

65. What form did the Egyptian god Apis take? **A bull**

66. Which Spanish-born bandleader, who popularised Latin American dance music, led a band called The Gigolos? **Xavier Cugat**

67. Whose Top Ten hits included *U Can't Touch This*, *Pray* and *Addams Groove*? **Hammer**

68. In the world of the arts, what was *The Filling Station*? **A ballet**

69. What was the name of Henry Williamson's salmon? **Salar**

70. How many sheets of paper are there now in a quire? **25**

71. If you were given kromesky would you drink it, rub it on your hair or eat it? **Eat it (Minced chicken rolled in bacon and fried)**

72. What is a hoggerel: a young pig, a young cow or a young sheep? **A young sheep**

73. Where did the Roman gods the Lares and Penates live? **In the home**

74. Who had a No 1 hit with *Belfast Child* in 1989? **Simple Minds**

75. Which England cricketer batted with a broken arm in plaster against the West Indies in a dramatic finish to a 1963 Test match? **Colin Cowdrey**

76. What did the Band of Hope pledge to be? **Totally abstinent**

77. Who played Picasso in the film *Surviving Picasso*?
Anthony Hopkins

78. To what is the adjective 'brackish' usually applied?
Water

79. Is a lorcha a boat, a fish or a fruit? **A boat**

80. In Norse mythology which giants were the enemies of the gods? **The Jötun**

81. Who was presenter and compere of *The Wheeltappers and Shunters Social Club*? **Colin Crompton**

82. Benjamin O Davis Sr was the first US negro to be a Supreme Court Judge, an astronaut or a general?
A general

83. How many basic formations are there in fingerprints?
Six

84. What nationality was Father Abraham of Smurf fame?
Dutch

85. Who wrote *Only When I Larf*, *London Match* and *Spy Hook*? **Len Deighton**

86. Who said on May 2nd, 1997: "When the curtain falls, it's time to get off the stage and that is what I propose to do."? **John Major**

87. Who managed the England football team for two months in 1974? **Joe Mercer**

88. Is an osmund a flowering fern, a precious stone or bone tissue? **A flowering fern**

89. Who played Johnny Depp's psychiatrist in the film *Don Juan DeMarco*? **Marlon Brando**

90. How many times were Rex Harrison, John Huston, Hedy Lamarr and Tom Mix married: 6, 7 or 8 times? **6 times**

91. What was the Joe Dolce Music Theatre's No 1 hit of 1981? **Shaddap Your Face**

92. Bubble and Saffron were characters in which TV series? **Absolutely Fabulous**

93. Which was the only naval engagement in which dreadnoughts faced each other? **Jutland**

94. Who beat England in the final of the 1992 Cricket World Cup? **Pakistan**

95. Who wrote the children's classic *The Cat In the Hat*? **Dr Seuss**

96. Is a caloyer a cheese-maker, a monk or a chimney? **A monk**

97. Who had Top Twenty hits with *Homburg* and *Pandora's Box*? **Procul Harum**

98. Who, in a famous play and film, travelled from Belle Reve to visit her sister in Elysian Fields? **Blanche Dubois**

99. What is the more common title of the ballet *The Girl with Enamel Eyes*? **Coppélia**

100. What did a lorimer make? **Spurs**

Quiz 40

1. In Buddhism and Hinduism what does the mandala represent? **The Universe**

2. Which country is separated from the Yucatan Peninsula by the Yucatan Channel? **Cuba**

3. True or false: Bel paese is an Italian wine? **False (It is cheese)**

4. Under what name did Romain de Tirtoff achieve fame as an Art Deco designer, especially for *Harper's Bazaar*?

Erté

5. Who traded places with Eddie Murphy in the film *Trading Places*? **Dan Aykroyd**

6. Which word means decision by chance, a plot of land and a considerable quantity? **Lot**

7. Who played Brian Stead in the TV series *The Troubleshooters*? **Geoffrey Keen**

8. In which sport were 'Dave and K' famous?

Rugby Union

9. If Yuba played the tuba and Pete the piccolo, what did Harry play? **Harmonica**

10. In what is meat stewed in bourguignon dishes? **Wine**

11. Which TV series featured a magic expert and a crime writer joining forces to investigate murder mysteries?

Jonathan Creek

12. Which Brazilian in 1972 became the youngest ever driver to win the World Motor Racing Championship?

Emerson Fittipaldi

13. Who played soldier of fortune Robert Dapes in the film *Cuba*? **Sean Connery**

14. In which industry would a tribble be used?

Paper-making (It is a drying-frame)

15. Which groups of islands are separated by The Minch and The Little Minch? **The Inner and Outer Hebrides**

16. Who had Top Ten hits with *Happy To Be On an Island in the Sun* and *When Forever Has Gone*? **Demis Roussos**

17. Which creatures are the world's largest invertebrates?

Giant squids

18. Is a bouquetin a sauce, a nosegay or a goat?   **A goat**

19. Who painted the famous portrait of Sir Winston Churchill which Mrs Churchill ordered to be destroyed after her husband's death?   **Graham Sutherland**

20. What was originally included in tins of baked beans (until World War II) to add flavour?   **A piece of pork**

21. Which part of the body is affected by diplopia?
      The eyes (You see double)

22. Who played the title role in the film *Young Bess*?
      Jean Simmons

23. Who was 'The Fat Owl of the Remove'?   **Billy Bunter**

24. Where would you find harpings: on a ship, on a barrel or in a barn?   **On a ship**

25. Name David Hasselhoff's character in TV's *Baywatch*.
      Mitch

26. What was a 'London Particular'?   **A fog**

27. True or false: The Spitfire brought down more aircraft than all other aircraft and ground defences together during the Battle of Britain?   **False (The Hurricane did)**

28. In a famous poem who "for all his foolish pranks was worshipped in the ranks"?   **'Mad' Carew**

29. In which sport was Rudy Hartono of Indonesia a World Champion?   **Badminton**

30. Who had Top Ten hits with *I Go To Sleep*, *Don't Get Me Wrong* and *Hymn To Her*?   **The Pretenders**

31. Which word means an LP holder, part of a garment and a straight beer glass?   **Sleeve**

32. Which bird is called the scobby in parts of Britain?
      The chaffinch

33. To the French it is boudin; the Swedes call it palt and the Italians sanguinaccio: what do we call it?   **Black pudding**

34. What is the shortest winning margin in rowing?
A canvas

35. Name the theme of the TV series *The Works*.   **The arts**

36. What is the pericarp of peas?   **The pod**

37. Who played Bela Lugosi in the the 1994 film *Ed Wood*?
Martin Landau

38. What has been defined since 1851 by Sir George Biddell Airy's transit circle?   **The meridian**

39. The island of Öland lies off the coast of which country?
Sweden

40. With what was the Anacreontic Society of the 18th century concerned: music, poetry or oratory?   **Music**

41. Which English monarch was once booed while driving down Ascot racecourse?   **Queen Victoria**

42. What sort of fruit is a russet?   **An apple**

43. What is the capital of Surinam?   **Paramaribo**

44. Which popular operetta has been produced in Hot, Cool, Swing and Black versions?   *The Mikado*

45. Which cigarette company signed a deal in 1974 with McLaren to paint their racing cars in the red and white of Marlboro?   **Philip Morris**

46. What would you have if you were leptorrhine?
A long, thin nose

47. Who had Top Ten hits with *Gotta Pull Myself Together* and *Attention To Me*?   **The Nolans**

48. Which 1997 TV serial, based on a Francis Durbridge 1960s script, starred Jennifer Ehle, Tim Dutton and Julia Walters? ***Melissa***

49. Who wrote the poem that begins: ''Miss Joan Hunter Dunn, Miss Joan Hunter Dunn / Furnish'd and burnish'd by Aldershot sun''? **John Betjeman**

50. What was the subject of the film *Tora! Tora! Tora!*? **The Japanese attack on Pearl Harbor**

51. Where are the Queen's Beasts, the Ice-House, the Ruined Arch and the Japanese Gateway? **Kew Gardens**

52. True or false: The Knowledge is contained in a pink book? **True (Though it is called the Blue Book!)**

53. Which game has been called 'chess played fast'? **Squash**

54. Who belong to the RICS? **Chartered surveyors**

55. What was the former name of *The Sun* newspaper? ***Daily Herald***

56. Is a nogging a small mug, a wall or a sack of tobacco leaves? **A wall**

57. From which sport did Gordy Howe retire at the age of 52 after 32 years playing at the top level? **Ice hockey**

58. Which company made the DB5 and DB7 cars? **Aston Martin**

59. Who starred in the films *The Goodbye Girl, The Competition* and *Mr Holland's Opus*? **Richard Dreyfuss**

60. Who had Top Twenty hits with *Eat Yourself Whole* and *10 Years Asleep*? **Kingmaker**

61. Who was the ibis-headed god of Ancient Egypt, scribe to the gods and inventor of writing? **Thoth**

62. Who played Peggy in the TV series *Keeping Mum*?
Stephanie Cole

63. True or false: Britain and the USA almost went to war in 1861? **True**

64. Of which sport did Mr Jingle say (in *Pickwick Papers*) "Capital game – smart sport – fine exercise – very."?
Cricket

65. What was described as "The Tory party at prayer"?
Church of England

66. Which North American lake has Fort Reliance, Fort Resolution, Snowdrift and Yellowknife on its shore?
Great Slave Lake

67. Which book was described by Arnold Bennett as "the longest sensational serial ever written"?
Oxford English Dictionary

68. Which foodstuff can follow Oxford, Cambridge, Gloucester, Suffolk, Lincolnshire and Cumberland?
Sausages

69. Of which country is Huascaran the highest mountain peak? **Peru**

70. Which famous trading people of ancient times sprang up around Tyre about 2700 BC? **Phoenicians**

71. Which club did David Ginola leave to join Tottenham Hotspur in 1997? **Newcastle United**

72. Which TV series featured Pauline McLynn as housekeeper Mrs Doyle? *Father Ted*

73. Spencer Gulf, Gulf St Vincent and Investigator Strait are off the coast of which country? **Australia**

74. What are a James Grieve and an Ellison Orange?
Apples

75. Who had Top Ten hits with *Boxer Beat* and *Just Got Lucky*? **Jo Boxers**

76. How many spas are there in England: 7, 8 or 9? **9**

77. In which film did Donald Pleasence discover cannibals living in disused London Underground tunnels? ***Death Line***

78. Which famous writer was known as 'The Chocolate Sailor' and 'Lady Rothermere's Fan'? **Ian Fleming**

79. Is a polymath a lie-detector, a sum with several answers or a very learned person? **A very learned person**

80. Where did the Greeks defeat the Persians in a land battle of 479 BC? **Plataea**

81. Which British football club beat Italian side Atalanta in September 1987 in the European Cup Winners Cup? **Merthyr Tydfil**

82. When did the first negro slaves arrive in America: 1502, 1522 or 1542? **1502**

83. Mozart, Elgar and Monteverdi all composed works with which 'royal' word in the title? ***Coronation***

84. In which Joyce Cary novel does the artist Gully Jimson appear? ***The Horse's Mouth***

85. What is measured by a chronoscope: the velocity of missiles, spaces in the spectrum or the accuracy of timepieces? **The velocity of missiles**

86. Which comedy game show was hosted by Tim Vine? ***Fluke***

87. Where exactly is the Knightwood Oak? **In the New Forest**

88. Which sport featured in the film *When We Were Kings*? **Boxing**

89. Who had a 1993 No 1 with *Dreams*? **Gabrielle**

90. What is the chemical symbol for Chromium? **Cr**

91. Which census first showed the population of the UK to be more than 50 million: 1941, 1951 or 1961? **1951**

92. Is a bottine a small bottle, a shepherd's shelter or a boot? **A boot**

93. In which city is the Royal Armouries Museum? **Leeds**

94. Which member of England's World Cup winning football team was banned from receiving FA Cup Final tickets for seven years in 1992? **Gordon Banks**

95. In which newspaper did Teddy Tail appear? *Daily Mail*

96. Which famous author espoused spiritualism and was duped by faked photographs of fairies? **Sir Arthur Conan Doyle**

97. Which statesman was MP for Old Bexley and Sidcup in the 1990s? **Edward Heath**

98. What colour is the ribbon on the George Cross? **Dark blue**

99. Who composed the light operas *A Princess of Kensington*, *Tom Jones* and *Fallen Fairies*? **Edward German**

100. Is niello a black alloy, an Italian marble or the smell of cooked meat? **A black alloy**